The Temple

GLORIFYING GOD IN YOUR EVERYDAY LIFE

*… YOUR BODY IS A **TEMPLE** OF THE HOLY SPIRIT…*
*THEREFORE **GLORIFY GOD** IN YOUR BODY.*
1 CORINTHIANS 6:19–20

LAURIE COLE

Production Coordinators: Janet Valentine, Pam Henderson

Layout and Design: Pam Henderson

Editorial Team: Lezli Busbee, Robin Cook, Kaye Davenport, Pat Habashy, Cathy Hipps, Kathy Howard, Janet Valentine, Lee Valentine

Cover Design & Artistic Consulting: Delynn Halloran

Graphic Artwork: Brittney Hood

Photography: Don and Mary Carico, Lakewood Photography

Third Edition—2010

Priority Ministries
Encouraging Women to Give God Glory & Priority

www.priorityministries.org

Dedication

To my beloved husband, Bill

You selflessly lead our family.
You constantly encourage and inspire me.
You consistently glorify God in all that you do.
Because you are a man of honor,
I honor you by dedicating this book to you.
I *love* you.

Acknowledgements

I think my dear friend, Nancy Campbell, said it best: *Every birth is different, and so is every child.* She made that statement after she'd heard of my struggle to "carry" and "give birth" to this (my second) Bible study. God used Nancy's wise words to comfort and encourage me throughout the writing process—bless you, beloved friend.

Now, as I joyously "deliver" this Bible study to you, dear sister, I want you to know about the many "midwives" (and some wonderful men, too) who selflessly assisted me throughout the birthing process:

Janet Valentine—My beloved friend and partner in ministry, Janet amazes me with her gifts of administration and leadership, blesses me with her positive, joyful spirit and fans my faith to follow God to parts unknown.

Pam Henderson—An awesome Godsend and cherished staff member, Pam selflessly gave many, *many* hours of her time and considerable talents to produce and design the pages of this workbook. Pam possesses the spirit of an angel and the patience of Job!

Lezli Busbee—A favorite friend and ministry partner, Lezli has a head for numbers and a heart for the Lord—what a beautiful blend! She also provided honest, valuable feedback as she conscientiously proofed every page of this workbook.

Lee Valentine—One of the most gracious, loving men I have ever known, once again Lee willingly volunteered to edit, critique, and proof the rough manuscripts of a *women's* Bible study. What a man!

Missy Krukiel and Nancy Campbell—These two mighty prayer warriors very likely spent more time praying for this project than anyone else. In addition, they also enlisted the **Priority Prayer Partners** to cover this project in prayer. Daily I witnessed God answer their prayers.

Paula Munroe—All throughout the writing process, I was keenly aware of the quiet, behind-the-scenes prayers of someone I dearly love and deeply respect. Bless you, Paula, for faithfully petitioning heaven on my behalf.

Joyce Shannon, Nancy Wilson, Jan Weede, Leslie Casper, Ashley Naylor, and Jackie Gieptner—This delightful "meals on wheels" team spoiled my entire family with their delicious dishes of home-cooked delicacies and allowed me to write more and cook *less!* When you girls publish your cookbook, I'll be first in line to buy it!

Pat and Labib Habashy—A godly couple who love and live God's Word, Pat and Labib's friendship, ministry, and prayers have blessed me immeasurably, and their wisdom and fellowship have nourished me immensely.

Carol Wroten and the WOW Class—My favorite place to be on Sunday mornings is with the wonderful women of WOW—my Sunday school class. Girls, every week that I'm with you I learn more about faith, hope, and love. How I thank God for what *you've* taught me.

Susan Gadd—A fellow writer, teacher, and friend, Susan taught my Sunday school class for two months in order to give me more time to focus on writing this study. The class fell in love with her and embraced her gracious messages—just as I knew they would.

Myra Davis—At a critical point in the process of writing this study, God prompted Myra to offer me a one-week sanctuary at her beautiful property on the banks of the Frio River in the Texas Hill Country. The landscape was inspirational, and the fellowship was, too.

Dr. John Morgan—My beloved pastor, Bro. John consistently inspires me to be about the Father's business and to provide living proof of a loving God to a watching world—which is a perfect description of his own life and ministry.

I also want to express my heartfelt thanks to the very special women of the **LifeTouch Bible Study** program at **Sagemont Church**. Your faith and support in participating in the pilot study meant more to me than you'll ever know. You prayed me through the writing process week by week, and you patiently waited on the next installment of the study with great grace. It is an honor and delight to study God's Word with sweet sisters like you. Yes ma'am, you girls really do *glo*!

Most importantly, I want to acknowledge and thank my guys—**Bill, David, Kevin, and J.J.** There is absolutely no way I could have completed this project without your love and support. Thanks for giving me the space I needed to write. But thanks even more for invading my space with your companionship and fun fellowship when I needed it most. I may be the only woman in a house full of men, but you guys make me feel like a queen. I love y'all *so much*.

About the Study

This workbook is an in-depth, topical Bible study. It is designed to enable you to "dig-in" to God's Word and experience the joy of discovering truth as the Holy Spirit tutors and teaches you. To facilitate your sensitivity and dependence upon the Spirit, each day you will be encouraged (through a verse from the Psalms) to begin your study in prayer. At the conclusion of each day's study, you will be instructed to record any insights the Holy Spirit has given you.

A good translation of the Bible will be essential as you do this study. The *New International Version,* the *New American Standard Bible,* the *King James Version,* or the *New King James Version* are all very accurate translations and are highly recommended. In this study, the author will primarily use the *New International Version* and the *New American Standard Bible.*

About the Author

Laurie Cole is the Founder and President of Priority Ministries, a ministry dedicated to encouraging women to give God glory and priority in their lives.

Raised in a strong Christian home, Laurie became a Christian at an early age. But in her early twenties, God tested and taught her the importance of truly giving Him priority in her life.

In 1985, Laurie enrolled in an in-depth women's Bible study. Encouraged by the older women who led the study, Laurie received training and began teaching and leading a group where God affirmed His call upon her life to teach.

Now, more than twenty-five years later, Laurie has taught dozens of Bible studies, and has spoken at numerous women's events and conferences. She has also written three other in-depth Bible studies: *There Is A Season, Beauty by The Book,* and *Beauty by The Book for Teens.* Her passion for God and hunger for His Word continues to grow.

A minister's wife, Laurie and her husband, Bill, serve the Lord at Sagemont Church in Houston, Texas, where he is the Associate Pastor of Worship and Praise. They have been married 35 years and have three sons, David, Kevin, and J.J., one beloved daughter-in-law, Stephanie, and three absolutely glorious grandchildren, Ezra, Juliette, and Caroline.

Contents

Introduction

There are certain sermons we never forget. Over twenty years ago, I heard one such sermon. It was entitled *What to Say When You Don't Know What to Say*, and it was delivered by Ron Dunn, a godly preacher who had grappled with that subject many times—just as you and I have. Ron is in heaven now, where all of life's questions have been eclipsed by the glory of God's presence. Yet even after all these years, I clearly remember the primary text of his memorable message:

> *Now My heart is troubled, and what shall I say? 'Father, save Me from this hour'? No, it was for this very reason I came to this hour. Father, glorify Your name.*
>
> —John 12:27–28

In the hours preceding His death, as Jesus sought to express His troubled heart in prayer, He asked this honest, transparent question: "what shall I say?" His answer to that question was, "Father, glorify Your name!" In Ron Dunn's excellent exegesis of this passage, he explained these four, brief words of Jesus—"Father, glorify Your name"—provide a way for us to pray within God's will, even when we are grappling with God's way. Though I heard that sermon only once long ago, its truth has ministered to me many, many times since.

"Father, glorify Your name." Through the years, I've learned that short, submissive prayer has a broader, wider application. Far more than just a prayer to be offered during days of uncertainty, "Father, glorify Your name," should be the *primary, ongoing prayer of our everyday life*. Why? Because we are God's temple, and glorifying God is the primary purpose of our life:

> *Or do you not know that your body is a temple of the Holy Spirit who is in you, whom you have from God, and that you are not your own? For you have been bought with a price: therefore glorify God in your body.*
>
> —1 Corinthians 6:19–20 *NASB*

Although you may live an ordinary, everyday life, *you* are no ordinary, everyday woman. You are God's temple and you have the supernatural ability to "glo"—to reflect the very glory of God. In fact, that is God's greatest goal for your life.

"Father, glorify Your name!" Immediately after Jesus prayed that prayer, the scriptures record God's response: "Then a voice came from heaven, 'I have glorified it, and will glorify it **again'**" (John 12:28).

Hours later, on Calvary's cross, God *was* glorified—*again*.

Dear sister, as you begin this study, I'm praying God will use it in such a way that He'll be glorified again, and again, and again. *"Father, glorify Your name."*

Your sister,

Laurie

The Temple: GOD'S GLORY VS. SELF GLORY OR GET OVER _____

Or do you not know that your body is a temple of the Holy Spirit who is in you, whom you have from God, and that you are not your own? For you have been bought with a price: therefore glorify God in your body.

—1 Corinthians 6:19–20 *NASB*

This verse answers the _____ _____ _____ of life:

1. _____ am I? I am ___ _____ of the Holy Spirit.

2. _____ am I? I _____ _____ belong to myself; I _____ ____ _____.

3. What is my _____? I am _____ to _____ _____.

This study will enable you to answer two more very important questions:

1. What does it mean to _____ _____ _____?

2. How can I _____ _____ in my _____ _____?

Chapter One: The Story of _____:

1. The _____ of man and woman. *Gen. 1:26–28*

   * _____ with God.

   * Oneness with _____ _____.

   * Oneness in _____

2. The _____ of man and woman. *Gen. 3:1–6*

   * Desire for _____ _____.

   * Desire for _____ apart from _____ = _____

   * RESULT: The desire for _____ _____ resulted in the _____ of

   _____ _____.

The Seven Deadly Sins of Women

1. Self _____   *says: _____

   * constant need to _____ and _____ the offenses we've suffered.

   * choice to maximize _____ and minimize _____.

   * it is the opposite of _____.

2. Self _____   *says: _____

   * constant need to focus on _____ I _____.

   * choice to maximize my _____ and minimize the _____ of others.

   * it is the opposite of _____.

3. Self _____ *says: _____

    *constant need to be _____, _____, or positioned so that others

    can see how _____ we are.

    *choice to do _____ so that we will look _____.

    *it is the opposite of _____.

4. Self _____ *says: _____

    *constant need to _____ for ourselves everything we can get even if others are

    _____.

    *choice to be a _____ instead of a _____.

    *it is the opposite of a _____.

5. Self _____ *says: _____

    *constant need to spend inordinate _____, energy, thought, and _____ on our

    _____.

    *choice to focus more on the importance of how we appear ____ _____ than

    on how we appear ____ _____.

    *it is the opposite of _____ _____ because it is _____ _____.

6. Self _____ *says: _____

    *constant need to live in a _____ of _____ and _____.

    *choice to beat ourselves up constantly over _____ _____ and _____.

    *it is the opposite of _____ because it is _____ in God's forgiveness.

7. Self _____ *says: _____

    *constant need to _____ ourselves as being _____ _____.

    *choice to believe our _____ _____ and perfections have made us

    _____ _____.

    *it is the opposite of _____ and a _____ spirit.

How can we get over _____ so that we can _____ _____?

   1.   By accepting the _____ of God through the _____ of Christ's _____.
         Rom. 5:8,12,19

   2.   By daily emptying _____ of _____ and by presenting our bodies to God
         as living sacrifices. *Rom. 12:1*

   3.   By living with a _____ mindset.

   RESULT: Restoration of _____ with God and the ability to _____ God.

Before you can ever be_____ _____ with His glory,
you must first be _____ _____ of self.

It's time for us to _____ _____ _____.

The Temple: GLORY!

Fame and fortune are the twin goals of an ever-increasing number of Americans every year. In fact, I think celebrity and wealth have become national obsessions. To prove my point, I present to you the following evidence: the current craze and rising popularity of reality TV shows and the countless numbers of people who, despite the risk of national humiliation, willingly and enthusiastically compete on these programs.

And I'll be honest. I have a little firsthand knowledge about reality shows. When my husband Bill and I are in couch potato mode, one of the programs we enjoy watching together is a reality show that has become a nationwide phenomenon. The show is *American Idol.* Millions of Americans tune in each week to watch a parade of individual contestants sing and perform before a panel of brutally honest judges in their quest to achieve stardom and its monetary rewards.

As each season of *American Idol* begins, the pool of talent is broad and vast. But despite the enormous number of super-star wannabes, what amazes me is just how few of them have the intangible yet distinct characteristics that will ultimately propel them to stardom. The judges on *American Idol* call it "star-quality," "self-possession," "presence," and "the it factor." It's what separates the singers from the stars. There are thousands of good singers, but only a handful of them possess the essential yet elusive qualities that set them apart from the crowd.

Even in today's celebrity-obsessed culture, stars are a rare commodity. In my entire lifetime, I don't think I've ever known or even met one single star. But I have met many individuals who possess some very tangible and distinct characteristics that literally set them apart from the crowd. These people are not "self-possessed," they're Spirit-possessed. The "presence" they exude isn't the result of their own perfect poise, but is instead the pristine presence of God in their lives.

Just who are these remarkable people? I'll tell you who they are. They're ordinary men and women who have been chosen and set apart by God in an extraordinary way. They are those rare, radiant Christians who glorify God in their everyday lives.

As Christians, we have been called and divinely enabled to glow like stars, in a sense, for God. We have been created to glorify our Creator. But unfortunately, just as there are thousands of good singers who fail to become an *American Idol* because they lack "star-quality," there also are thousands of Christians who fail to glorify God because they do not allow the light of Christ to glow within them. And glorifying God is what separates the Christian from the Christlike.

THIS WEEK'S
KEY PRINCIPLE:

We glorify God in our everyday lives by desperately seeking Him, and by daily depending upon Him.

The Temple

I believe God has given each of us a stage—our everyday lives—so that we can perform before an audience He has hand-picked for us—our family, friends, co-workers, and everyone whose life intersects ours—in order to make Himself known in a way that brings Him glory. Jesus said it like this: "let your light shine before men in such a way that they may see your good works, and glorify your Father who is in heaven" (Matthew 5:16).

Reality shows will come and go. Most of the winners and the stars they produce will flicker and fade, as will the fortunes they gained. But the final reality is this: One day we will all stand upon the most important stage of all, but we will not perform or compete. Instead we will face an audience of One, and that One will judge us according to the performance we gave during our time on earth. All that will matter then is whether our brief, earthly life glorified Him in an eternal and everlasting way.

Eternity, the unseen reality—more real than any reality show—is what really matters. God's reward—more precious than earthly fame and fortune—is the goal we must seek. So, from this day on, let's commit to giving God the performance of a lifetime by glorifying Him in our ordinary, everyday lives.

Simply put, my sister, *you glo, girl!*

Day One

As you begin the very first day of this study, I want to encourage you to begin in prayer. Prayer is often the most neglected area in our spiritual lives. And in a study like this, it's easy to just grab your Bible, open your workbook and jump right in and do your homework. I know. Been there, done that myself. But I've learned what a **big** difference even a **little** prayer can make.

To encourage you in your prayer life, I'll begin each day of this study with a few words of exhortation and a brief reading from the Psalms. So still your heart, dear sister, for the first few moments of your study each day and enjoy some fellowship with your Father in prayer.

1. This week you will begin the process of discovering what it means to be a temple that glorifies God. Before you begin your study, please read the following Psalm, then prayerfully ask God to make praising and glorifying Him an ongoing, ever-growing reality in your life.

    I will praise You, O Lord my God, with all my heart;
    I will glorify Your name forever. Psalm 86:12

2. The key verses for this study (1 Corinthians 6:19–20) are printed for you. Read and begin memorizing these verses.

Or do you not know that your body is a temple of the Holy Spirit who is in you, whom you have from God, and that you are not your own? For you have been bought with a price: therefore glorify God in your body.

—1 Corinthians 6:19–20 NASB

3. Please personalize 1 Corinthians 6:19–20 by filling in the blanks in the paragraph below.

> My body is the _____ of the Holy Spirit who is _____ me and has been given to me from _____. I am not my _____, because I have been _____ with a price. As a result, I am to _____ _____ in my body.

4. As Christians, we are God's temple. Does that truth awe and confound you? God lives within us. When I think about that, it overwhelms me. It humbles me. And yet, at the same time, it makes me want to jump up and down! My sister, we are *God's temple!* Take a few moments to let the truth of 1 Corinthians 6:19–20 sink deep into your heart and mind. Meditate upon that verse, then respond as the Spirit leads you—even if that means you have to get up out of your chair and jump for joy.

5. As God's temple, we have a very high calling. That calling is to glorify God. In the weeks ahead, we will be learning how to glorify God through our daily lives. But before we go any further, we need to take a look at ourselves and examine the various components of our lives. On the following chart, please honestly describe how you would currently define or describe yourself in each of the categories listed.

Defining Myself:

My personality
My spiritual life
My roles and responsibilities
My relationships

My physical body
My successes
My failures
My current joys
My current challenges
My possessions

6. The categories on the chart you just completed represent the many components that make up most of our lives. Very often we define ourselves by one or more of these categories. As you review your chart, please list (in order of their influence) the top five categories that most influence and define who you are right now:

    # 1 _____

    # 2 _____

    # 3 _____

    # 4 _____

    # 5 _____

7. Now let's briefly look at God's perception of us. How does He define and describe us? Please read the following scriptures. Note how God defines you and how and why He created you.

    a.   Psalm 8:3–5

b.   Isaiah 43:7

c.   Ephesians 2:19–22 (This is how God sees His people, the church.)

d.   2 Thessalonians 2:13–14

e.   1 Peter 2:9

8.   Finally, take what you've learned today before the Lord—especially your top
     five list (from Question 6). Ask Him to show you whether you are glorifying
     Him in these key areas of your life. Please record any insights He has revealed
     to you today.

_____

_____

_____

_____

_____

_____

_____

_____

_____

— ❧ *Day Two* ❧ —

1.   God is so good to us! And today's Psalm is a beautiful reminder of His
     goodness. After you've read the Psalm, please spend a few minutes in prayer
     thanking Him for the light, protection, grace, and glory He has given you.
     Ask Him to show you how to glorify Him through your life today.

For the Lord God is a sun and shield;
The Lord gives grace and glory;
No good thing does He withhold from those who walk uprightly.
Psalm 84:11 *NASB*

In the scriptures you studied yesterday, you learned that you are God's creation, possession, and temple, and you are called to glorify God. But **what does it mean to glorify God?** That, my sister, is the most important question of this entire study, and that is where we'll begin our study today.

As I began my research to prepare to write this study, one of the first things I did was to investigate the biblical definition of the words "glory" and "glorify." For this study, we'll be using the definitions from *Nelson's Illustrated Bible Dictionary*. Nelson's definitions are complete, accurate, and easy to understand. But most significantly for us, these definitions will help us answer the **big** question: **what does it mean to glorify God?** Please read Nelson's definitions below, and observe the three primary ways the word "glory" is used:

> **Glory**—beauty, power, or honor; a quality of God's character that emphasizes His greatness and authority. The word is used in three senses in the Bible:
>
> 1. God's moral beauty and perfection of character. This divine quality is beyond man's understanding. All people "fall short" of it.
>
> 2. God's moral beauty and perfection as a visible presence. While God's glory is not a substance, at times God does reveal His perfection to man in a visible way. Such a display of the presence of God is often seen as fire or dazzling light, but sometimes as an act of power.
>
>   Since the close of the Old Testament, the glory of God has been shown mainly in Christ and in the members of His church. Christ now shares His divine glory with His followers, so that in their lives Christians are being transformed into the glorious image of God. Believers will be fully glorified at the end of time in God's heavenly presence. There the glory of God will be seen everywhere.
>
> 3. Praise. At times God's glory may mean the honor and audible praise which His creatures give to Him.
>
> **Glorify**—to magnify God through praising His name and honoring His commandments. Jesus also glorified His Father through His perfect obedience and His sacrificial death on our behalf.[1]

2. As you have just read, the word "glory" often refers to God's divine nature and attributes.[2] Now take a few moments for some prayerful reflection, and ask the Lord to remind you of His divine character. As He reveals specific characteristics to you, write them on the following list. To help you get started, I've written a couple of God's attributes on your list already. If you need a little more help and inspiration, I think it would do your heart good to read one of David's songs of praise, Psalm 145, as well as a couple of the hymns of heaven found in Revelation 4:8–11, and Revelation 15:3–4. You'll find many of God's glorious attributes recorded in these scriptures.

The Attributes of His Glory

eternal _____   *creator* _____

_____   _____

_____   _____

_____   _____

_____   _____

_____   _____

_____   _____

_____   _____

_____   _____

_____   _____

_____   _____

_____   _____

3. According to Nelson's definition, God's glory is also visibly revealed.[3] In Exodus 19–20, God revealed His glory in a very dramatic way to the children of Israel. Please read Exodus 19:9–12, 16–19, and Exodus 20:1–19, then answer the following questions:

    a. How did God visibly reveal His glory in this passage?

    b. What attributes did God reveal about Himself through His actions?

c. Where were the people standing as God spoke to them, and where was God? What does this tell you about God's glory and His relationship to the children of Israel?

4. You just saw how God visibly revealed His glory to the Israelites. But does God still reveal His glory to people in the same way today and, if so, how? Please answer this question by reading the following scriptures and by noting what you learn about God's glory.

a. Psalm 19:1

b. Romans 1:18–25

5. Based upon what you learned from Romans 1, what are the consequences of refusing to acknowledge God's glory?

6. *Nelson's Illustrated Bible Dictionary* also defines God's glory as praise and adoration given to Him.[4] Please read Psalm 148 and answer the following questions:

a. According to this Psalm, who (or what) is commanded to praise and glorify God? Name the various groups mentioned in this Psalm.

b. Now think about this: in addition to the fact that all of these groups are commanded to praise God, what else do they all hold in common?

7. As you conclude your time of study today, reflect upon the various ways God has revealed His glory to you. Which of His attributes has He displayed or expressed to you recently? How have you visibly seen His mighty deeds? Give Him glory and praise today by recording your insights.

_____

_____

_____

_____

_____

_____

Day Three

1. Before you begin to delve into God's Word today, bow your head and prayerfully give Him an offering of praise and thanksgiving.

Ascribe to the Lord the glory due His name;
bring an offering, and come into His courts. Psalm 96:8

I truly believe one of the biggest obstacles we face as we seek to glorify God is that we have forgotten just how glorious He is. Most of our waking hours are full to the brim with the routine responsibilities and activities of our daily lives. In our haste and hurry, we're often too busy and self-consumed to see the glory of God. We walk right past it every day—but we don't see it. And because we don't see it, we've forgotten the glory of the One we consistently and routinely refer to as "God." Yet every day without fail, our faithful, invisible God visibly makes His glory known.

Today I want to take you far away from your busy life and crazy calendar. We are going to escape for a few minutes from our current roles, routines, and responsibilities. The purpose of this much needed day trip is to help us gain a fresh glimpse of God's glory. Don't you long to see His glory? I do, too. And I believe God desires to show us His splendor and majesty in a brand new way *every* day.

We'll be going back in time to join a man who shared our longing to see the glory of God. Although he is recognized and remembered as one of the great forefathers of our faith, Scripture also records that he was very much like us: human. This man is Moses, and we are about to vicariously join him at a time in his life when he beheld the glory of God. This journey will require us to engage all of our senses as we try to imagine what it would have been like for Moses to experience this phenomenal event. As you read the following scriptures, try your very best to walk in Moses' "sandals." I have said enough for now. Incline your heart and tune your ear to the Spirit. May you catch a glimpse of God's glory through your journey into His Word today.

2. In order to gain a greater understanding of all that Moses was experiencing at this point in his life, please read Exodus 24:12, 15–18, 32:1–20, 25–35. Then answer the following questions:

a. According to Exodus 24, where was Moses, who was he with, and how long was he there?

b. According to Exodus 32, what was Moses' first response when God told Moses He was going to destroy the children of Israel because of their sin (see verses 11–13)? What does Moses' response reveal about his leadership and heart?

c. When Moses descended from Mt. Sinai and saw the Israelites' idolatry and sin firsthand, how did he respond (see Exodus 32:19–20, 25–29)? What emotions did he express, and what does his response reveal to you about Moses?

3. Exodus 32:7–29 represents the events of one single day in Moses' life as the leader of Israel. Prior to this, Moses had been in intimate communion alone with God for forty days and nights. Think about each of the following questions, and honestly and candidly record your answers to them:

a. How do you think Moses would have described or summarized this particular day if he were recording in a journal?

b. How do you think it would have compared to his journal entries from the previous forty days?

c. How do you think Moses felt as a leader?

4. Things continued to grow worse for Moses and his people. Please read Exodus 33:1–3, and record the distressing news God gave to Moses (v. 3)

5. Exodus 33:12–17 gives us the transcript of a very intense conversation between God and Moses. Please carefully read this passage, and answer the following questions:

a. As Moses meets with God, what burden and concern did he express to God (v. 12)?

b. What wonderful news did God give Moses (v. 14)?

    c.   According to verses 15–16, what need does Moses reiterate to God, and what reason does he give for being so desperate for God to meet this need?

6. Although God granted all of Moses' requests, Moses had one final request. Please read the remainder of this chapter (Exodus 33:18–23), and answer the following questions:

    a.   What was Moses' final request of God (v. 18)?

    b.   As you think about all that Moses experienced on the previous day (Exodus 32:1–29), how might those experiences have led him to make such a request?

7. In tomorrow's study, we will ascend the mountain with Moses to see God's glory. But as we close our time of study today, let me ask you some very personal questions:

    a.   Although you do not have the same leadership responsibilities Moses had, what responsibilities *has* God given to you? Who is looking to you for leadership? What challenges are you currently facing?

    b.   What characteristics in Moses' life do you most need in yours?

c. Please check the box that best describes your current daily awareness of and dependence upon God's presence in your life:

❒ I am aware and dependent upon God's presence and power in my life from the moment I wake in the morning until I fall asleep at night.

❒ I am usually aware of God's presence in my life throughout most of my day, but I am not always dependent upon His power until I am faced with the daily challenges of life.

❒ I am aware of God's presence in my life most of the time, but I usually rely upon my own strength.

❒ I am somewhat aware of God's presence in my life, but I experience very little of His power in my daily life.

❒ I am not usually aware of God's presence in my life until I am faced with challenges that are beyond my control and strength. At that point, I cry out to God to ask for His help.

❒ I see God's presence and strength in other people's lives, but I do not consistently experience His presence or strength in my own life.

My sister, I believe one of the reasons Moses was so *intimate* with God was because Moses was so *dependent* upon God's presence and God's power. Faced with the constant, overwhelming challenges of leading God's people, Moses responded with a constant, overwhelming hunger to know and experience God.

Insights

8. Based upon your response to the previous question (Question 8c), are you completely dependent upon God's presence and power in your daily life? Do you have an overwhelming hunger to know and experience God in an intimate way? Take a few minutes to record your answers to these questions, and express the desire of your heart to God.

_____

_____

_____

_____

_____

_____

_____

   I cannot conclude today's homework until I've encouraged you to do one more thing. Dear sister, if you're concerned or confused because you're just not experiencing the daily, ongoing power of God's presence in your life, I want to ask you to turn to page 221 and read the article entitled *A Change of Heart*. You truly *can* experience God's presence and power in your life. The One who loves you most and knows you best desires to enjoy an intimate relationship with you. Find out how right now by reading *A Change of Heart*.

Day Four

1. Before you begin your time of study, please read the following Psalm. It was written at a very desperate time in David's life. Whatever cares or concerns you may be facing today, bow your head and prayerfully acknowledge God's presence and protection upon your life just as David did. Glory in God's provision for you today.

But You, O Lord, are a shield around me,
my glory, and the One who lifts my head high. Psalm 3:3

Yesterday we began a vicarious walk with Moses during a very challenging time in his life. We watched his heart break as God told him of the sin of his people and of His plans to destroy them. We listened to Moses intercede and plead for God to spare their lives.

Next we witnessed Moses' compassion turn to anger as he saw with his own eyes the golden calf and the idolatry of his people. The stone tablets were shattered. The golden calf was ground to powder. Aaron was confronted and called into account. We listened as Moses rallied the people to repentance and righteousness and declared death and destruction to those who would not repent. We read the grim statistics and learned that approximately 3000 men were immediately executed in what certainly must have been a gruesome bloodbath. And just imagine, all of this happened to Moses in *one day*.

Usually, even when we've had a bad day, and even when we've gone to bed discouraged, we awake the next morning, and things appear better and brighter in the light of a brand new day. Although that sunny scenario may hold true for us most of the time, in Moses' case it did not. When Moses woke up the next morning, things did *not* get better. In fact, things only grew worse.

The morning after the golden calf incident, Moses met with God and faithfully began interceding for the Israelites asking God to forgive them. God responded, but he refused Moses' requests. The guilty would *not* be forgiven—instead, they would be judged. And as if that were not bad enough, God further announced that He would no longer accompany Moses and the Israelites on their journey to the Promised Land. God had finally had it with them. He could no longer bear to be near them. God's terse, matter-of-fact pronouncement was then followed by a devastating plague. No, it definitely wasn't looking like the beginning of a very promising day for Moses.

Then Moses revealed why he must certainly be one of God's favorites (OK, I know God doesn't play favorites, but indulge me here for a moment). Moses had just experienced one of the worst days of his life, and now he's faced with an uncertain future full of people who cannot be trusted. Here's my question for you: If you'd been Moses, what would you have done next? As you ponder your answer, please keep in mind, Moses had options. He had choices. And he was human—just like you.

Yet in the midst of these extremely grim and difficult circumstances, let me tell you what Moses did: He did exactly what he *always* did—*he went to the tent.* Moses went to the place where he consistently met one-on-one with God. And when he entered, the people stood and watched as God's majestic presence descended in the form of a cloud upon a humble tent which housed within it a very humble man. That morning, as he went to the tent, Moses showed his people that his priority—in good times and in bad—was to *seek God's presence.* And that morning, by God's gracious example, the Lord revealed His desire to experience intimate fellowship with man. Suddenly, a day that had once looked hopeless became hopeful.

The dialogue of Moses' meeting with God in the tent is found in Exodus 33:12–18. Over and over in this passage, Moses expressed the primary concern of his heart to God. What follows is my own personal paraphrase of Moses' words: "God, You've told us to continue our journey to the Promised Land. But Lord, if You don't go with us, we don't want to go. We know full well the only thing we have going for us is Your presence. Your presence is the only thing that sets us apart from every other nation on the earth. God, how will the other nations know we're Your people if Your presence isn't visibly with us?"

You know what I think? I think Moses knew something that far too many of us have either forgotten or have come to take for granted. Moses knew that *God's presence is absolutely essential in every step we take and in every mile of every journey we make.* Moses not only recognized that he desperately needed God's presence, but Moses also desperately depended upon God's presence in his day-to-day life—which, of course, leads me to ask this question: Do we?

There is much we can learn from Moses' example. So let's return once again to the tent where Moses is meeting with God. Let's listen carefully to their conversation. A day that began with the terrible news of God's judgment is about to end with the promising words of God's goodness. Pick up your Bible. Grab your pen. A new day will soon dawn. Glory is on its way, and we don't want to miss it!

2. Please read and review the request Moses made of God in Exodus 33:13, and answer the following questions:

   a. There are three parts in Moses' request. These three parts are listed for you below. Using your own words, please paraphrase what you believe each of these statements means. Also, please note any significance you see regarding the order in which they are stated.

      1) *"teach me Your ways"*

2) *"so that I may know You"*

3) *"and continue to find favor with You."*

b.   What does this reveal to you about Moses' heart and life? What kind of relationship did he desire to have with God?

3. As Moses and God continue their meeting, Moses makes one final request. You studied it briefly yesterday, but please read Exodus 33:18–23, and answer the following questions:

a.   What was Moses' final request (v. 18)?

b.   Please record God's response (vv. 19–23) by answering three questions:

What will Moses see? _____

What will Moses hear? _____

What will Moses not see? _____

c.   According to verse 21, what does Moses have to do in order to see God's glory?

4. Now I want you to do something that I hope will enable you to experience as fully as possible what it might have been like to ascend Mt. Sinai with Moses to see God's glory. Keeping in mind God's instructions to Moses from Exodus 33:18–23, please read Exodus 34:1–8. As you mentally review what Moses saw and heard that day, try to recapture his experience by journaling (in the first person, as though you were doing this yourself) what he might have written that day. I've given you a few words to help you get started.

Early this morning, I arose from my slumber and began a day that would

_____

_____

_____

_____

_____

_____

_____

_____

_____

_____

_____

_____

_____

_____

5. When God allowed Moses to see His glory, God also enabled Moses to know Him in a more intimate way. What did Moses learn about God's glorious character that day (Exodus 34:6–7)? Please write these attributes on the list provided.

The Attributes of His Glory

6. After seeing God's glory, Moses remained with God on the mountain for forty days and forty nights. When Moses descended from the mount, the sons of Israel immediately noticed something unique about Moses. Please read Exodus 34:29–35, then answer the following questions:

    a. What did the Israelites notice about Moses, and how did they respond (v. 30)?

    b. Was Moses aware of this (v. 29)?

    c. What specifically had caused this to happen to Moses (v. 29)?

    d. As you saw in verses 34–35, this phenomenon happened to Moses more than once. What caused this to happen each time?

    e. When this happened, what would Moses do (vv. 33–35)?

    f. What did the Israelites see visibly manifested on Moses' countenance? Need a hint? It's a five-letter word, and it's the title of this week's lesson.

7. As you reflect upon Moses' encounters with God in the Tent of Meeting and on the mountain, and as you think about how these encounters affected Moses' life, what insights has the Holy Spirit shown you that you can apply to your own life?

Insights

_____

_____

_____

_____

_____

_____

_____

The Temple

— Day Five —

1. Today's Psalm was written by David, but it sure sounds like it could have been written by Moses. Begin your study time in prayer by asking God to give you a heart like David and Moses. Ask Him to increase your desire to live in His presence and see His glory.

> *I love the house where You live, O Lord,*
> *the place where Your glory dwells.* Psalm 26:8

Yesterday you watched Moses ascend Mt. Sinai to see God's glory as you studied Exodus 33–34. As he descended the mountain forty days later, the evidence of Moses' encounter with God was written upon, not only the two stone tablets he carried, but it was also "written" upon his face. God's glory visibly shone from Moses' countenance.

In a beautiful way, Moses' glowing face has application for us today. All throughout this study, I will be exhorting you with these words: You glo, girl! Now when I say that, please know I don't mean you're to glow literally, like Moses did. I'm simply using the word "glo" as an abbreviation for the word "glorify." When I say, "You glo, girl," I'm encouraging you to glorify God. But I'm also using the word "glo" as an illustration because, as Christians, we are called to be lights in this world. Our lives should visibly reflect and reveal the glory of the One who inhabits us—which should remind us of the scripture we began memorizing on Day One:

> *Or do you not know that your body is a temple of the Holy Spirit*
> *who is in you, whom you have from God, and that you are not your*
> *own? For you have been bought with a price: therefore glorify God*
> *in your body.*
>
> —1 Corinthians 6:19–20 *NASB*

As God's temple, we should glow. In the weeks ahead, we'll be studying and learning many specific ways we can glorify God. But for today, I want to help you understand how Moses' glowing face applies to us. Sister, we may not literally glow as Moses did but—now get ready because this next part is almost too good to be true—the glory God has given us is *even better* than the glory the children of Israel saw upon Moses' face! Isn't that amazing?! And doesn't that make you want to learn why the glory we have is greater than the glory Moses had? I sure hope so, because that will be the focus of our study today.

My sister, as you complete this first week's lesson, I'm praying God will give you a deeper appreciation for all that He's given you and a greater desire to glow for Him than you've ever had before.

2. Your focus today will be on 2 Corinthians 3. Please read this entire chapter slowly and purposefully. Observe the difference between the glory of Moses and The Law (the Old Covenant), and the glory of the New Testament believer (the New Covenant).

3. The following chart is based on the chapter you just read: 2 Corinthians 3. On this chart, you can clearly see the differences between the glory of Moses and The Law (the Old Covenant) and the glory of the New Testament believer (the New Covenant). Please take a few moments to study—and to rejoice in—the contrasts between Old Covenant and New Covenant.

The Glory of Moses and The Law vs.	**The Glory of the New Testament Believer**
1) v. 3 written by God on tablets of stone	1) v. 3 written by the Spirit on tablets of human hearts
2) v. 6 of the letter which kills	2) v. 6 of the Spirit which gives life
3) v. 7 came with glory	3) v. 8 came with even more glory
4) v. 9 it condemned men	4) v. 9 it made men righteous
5) v. 10 has no glory now	5) v. 10 has surpassing glory
6) v. 13 its glory was fading away	6) v. 18 its glory grows as we are being transformed

4. You've just seen how the glory of the New Testament believer surpasses the Old Testament glory of Moses and The Law. Please answer the following questions as you look at 2 Corinthians 3 once more:

   a. According to verses 2–3, is God's presence in our lives visible to others? Please explain your answer and include words from these verses in your explanation.

   b. According to verses 3, 6, 8, and 17–18, please explain the source of the believer's glory.

   c. According to verse 13, why did Moses cover his glowing face?

   d. According to verses 14–16, where is this "veil" today and how can it be removed?

e.   Please read verse 18, then check the box/boxes that are true about you.

And we, who with unveiled faces all reflect the Lord's glory are being transformed into His likeness with ever-increasing glory, which comes from the Lord, who is the Spirit.

—2 Corinthians 3:18

❑   I am a reflection of God's glory.

❑   I am being transformed into His likeness with ever-increasing glory.

5. Now let's take a brief look at an Old Testament passage written by David: Psalm 24:3–4. These verses are so appropriate in light of what we've studied this week. Please read them, and answer the following questions:

a.   What was David's question?

b.   What was David's answer?

c.   What about you? Is there anything hindering you from intimate fellowship with God? If so, what is it?

If you would like to enjoy fellowship and intimacy with God once again, you must seek "clean hands and a pure heart" (Psalm 24:4). You can do this in the same way David did—through confession and repentance of your sin. If you're ready to do this right now, please read Psalm 32:1–5, and follow David's example. Rejoice in God's forgiveness and in restored fellowship with Him.

6. This week we've seen how Moses diligently sought God's presence and desperately desired to know God intimately. As a result, he not only witnessed God's glory, he reflected God's glory. Please use the following words to begin journaling a prayer to the Lord that expresses the desire of your heart as a result of what He's revealed to you this week.

My heart's prayer today is that...

_____

_____

_____

_____

_____

_____

_____

_____

_____

_____

My sister, as we fight the ongoing daily battle against our own fleshly desires for glory and gain, may these words become our constant cry:

Not to us, O Lord, not to us but to Your name be the glory.
—Psalm 115:1

Oh Lord, may we always and only glo for You!

The Temple: DESPERATE BUT NOT DESPAIRING

Or do you not know that your body is a temple of the Holy Spirit who is in you, whom you have from God, and that you are not your own? For you have been bought with a price: therefore glorify God in your body.

—1 Corinthians 6:19–20 *NASB*

Key Principle: *We glorify God in our everyday lives*
by _____ _____ *Him, and by daily* _____ *upon Him.*

How does God, most often, teach us to _____ _____ for Him?

Two Primary Ways:

1. Through the _____ _____ we experience at various seasons throughout our lives.

    Example: Moses—*Exodus 24:12–18; 32:19–34:8*

    Moses *didn't* _____ _____ _____ _____.

    Moses *did* seek God _____ and _____.

    Results: He saw the _____ of God.

    He _____ the _____ of God to others.

    He _____ God through the extraordinary challenges of life.

    Example: _____—*Psalm 63*

2. Through the _____ _____ we experience in day-to-day life.

    Example: Moses—*Numbers 27:1–11, 36:1–10*

    Moses didn't _____ _____ only in seasons of extraordinary challenges.

    Moses also sought God _____ even in the _____ challenges of his daily life.

    Results: He received God's glorious _____ and_____.

    He reflected God's _____ to others.

    He glorified God through the _____challenges of day-to-day life.

    Do you want to glorify God through the _____ of your life?
    If so, be _____ without _____!

Glo, Girl!

The Temple: SHINE!

Chances are, if I asked you to complete the following sentence by filling in the blank, you probably wouldn't need a half-second before you'd have the answer. So, if you're ready, here's the sentence:

You can never be too rich or _____ _____.

Did you get the answer? Sure you did! It's that popular little phrase, "You can never be too rich or **too thin**." And, although it may be shallow and a cliché, this silly saying has become a full-blown philosophy for millions of women today.

Surely you would agree that our culture is consumed by the desire for physical perfection. You know: perfect skin, perfect thighs, perfect hair, perfectly flat tummies, perfect noses, all held together by a perfect body that is the exact, perfect weight. The emphasis may be merely external, but the beauty, fitness, fashion, and cosmetic surgery industries are enjoying wild financial profits because of our dream and desire for physical perfection.

Now please don't get me wrong. I do think our physical bodies are very important, and I'll even confess to being pretty well-stocked when it comes to wrinkle cream. It's just that I think the increasing value and focus we're placing upon our bodies is totally contrary to God's perspective. The world may *say*, "Beauty is only skin deep," but the reality is we live in a *very* "skin deep" world. And the ideals and values of the world have enticed and entangled many Christians, as well.

Personally, I think it's high time for us to take our focus off the perfect faces and perfect bodies we're constantly exposed to on television screens and magazine covers. It's time for us to quit comparing ourselves to the world's standards and ideals. We don't need a new weight loss formula and we don't need to look like we're twenty when we're fifty. What we need is a good, healthy dose of God's Word. What we need is the truth that will finally set us free from the shallow standards of this world.

This week let's ditch the superficial philosophy of "you can never be too rich or too thin" and let's embrace what God Himself has said about us: "we are His workmanship" (Ephesians 2:10). And no matter what shape or size you are, that's a one-size-fits-all verse.

THIS WEEK'S
KEY PRINCIPLE:

We glorify God in our everyday lives by reflecting His glory through pure and holy living.

Day One

1. As we seek to reflect God's glory and to be "transformed into His likeness with ever increasing glory" (2 Corinthians 3:18), we must follow Moses' example (as we studied last week) by passionately depending upon His presence and by diligently spending time with Him in prayer and fellowship.

Spend some time alone with God in prayer right now. Ask Him to use the time you spend in His Word today to give you light and truth that will lead you to a closer walk with Him.

*Send forth Your light and Your truth,
let them guide me; let them bring me to Your holy mountain,
to the place where You dwell.* Psalm 43:3

2. Let's begin this week's study with a review of our key verses from 1 Corinthians 6:19–20. You began memorizing it last week, and it's partially printed below. Use your memory to fill in the following blanks for this verse. If needed, please feel free to use your Bible.

> *Or do you not know that your body is a _____ of the _____ _____ who is in you, whom you have from God, and that you are _____ _____ _____? For you have been _____ with a _____: therefore _____ God in your _____.*

—1 Corinthians 6:19–20 *NASB*

3. There are two other passages in Corinthians that are very similar to our key verses. These two passages are listed below. Please use your Bible to read them, then write them in the space provided.

a. 1 Corinthians 3:16

b. 2 Corinthians 6:16

4. Now I have two questions that I just want you to think about:

- Why did the apostle Paul (the author of 1 & 2 Corinthians) repeat himself *three times* as he wrote to this specific group of people?
- What is compelling Paul to question and remind them that they are God's temple?

Finding the answers to these questions will be the focus of our study today. But before you begin to answer them, there's something you need to know. Paul's concern and commands weren't written solely for the sake of the Corinthians. Please read 1 Corinthians 1:2, and answer the following questions:

a.   Who else was Paul addressing when he wrote this letter?

b.   Do Paul's concerns and commands apply to the church today? Please circle your answer.

(Yes)   No

c.   Do Paul's concerns and commands apply to you? Please circle your answer.

(Yes)   No

5.   Let's discover now why Paul repeated himself (in 1 Corinthians 3:16–17, 6:19–20, and 2 Corinthians 6:16) and what compelled him to remind his readers that they are God's temple. To gain a clearer picture of what prompted Paul to write these two letters, please read the following passages. Summarize on the chart the issues of concern Paul had with the church at Corinth and the effect they had upon God's "temple." As you read each passage, please note: depending upon the context, the "temple" may refer to the individual believer or to the corporate church body.

Read & Study	Issues of Concern	Effect Upon God's Temple
1 Cor. 1:10–17 & 30–31		
1 Cor. 3:1–17		
1 Cor. 3:21–23 & 4:1–7		

Read & Study	Issues of Concern	Effect Upon God's Temple
1 Cor. 5:1–8		
1 Cor. 6:1–8		
1 Cor. 6:12–20		
2 Cor. 6:14–7:1		

6. How would these issues affect God's reputation and glory?

7. We've seen the issues and problems within the church at Corinth. But now we need to examine our own lives. I realize this may be very hard to do, but please ask the Holy Spirit to examine your heart thoroughly as you read the following list. Then humbly and honestly, as the Spirit prompts you, place a checkmark in each box that represents a current area of struggle for you.

    ❑   I am struggling with another Christian about an issue that has divided us.

    ❑   I struggle with focusing more on my favorite preachers and teachers of God's Word and trying to imitate them than focusing on Christ and desiring to imitate Him.

    ❑   I struggle with pride in my spiritual life, and sometimes I "pat myself on the back" when I compare my own spiritual maturity with that of other believers.

    ❑   I struggle with a lack of consistent spiritual growth.

    ❑   I struggle with compromise and immorality, and I am aware there are areas in my life that are impure.

    ❑   I struggle with confronting other Christians about their sin, and I usually keep silent even when I know I should speak truthfully to them.

    ❑   I have taken another Christian to court about a legal matter.

    ❑   I have become involved in a long-term partnership (either business or personal) with someone who is not a Christian.

    ❑   I struggle with compromising my Christian principles because of the influence and pressure I feel from my relationships with unbelievers.

8. If you checked any of the boxes in the previous question, I want you to ask yourself one more thing: How does this affect your intimacy with God and your ability to reflect His glory?

    The areas of struggle listed in Question 7 are the same issues that grieved and concerned Paul about the Corinthians. And why was he so concerned? Because these issues—these sins—were preventing them from glorifying God through their individual lives and through their church. The application for us is obvious. The sins they struggled with are the same sins we continue to struggle with in our own lives and churches. And, most importantly, *these are the very same issues that prevent us and our churches from glorifying God in our world today.*

9. As you meditate upon what you've studied today, please journal anything the Holy Spirit is leading you to do, and then *do it*.

_____

_____

_____

_____

_____

_____

_____

_____

— ❦ *Day Two* ❦ —

1. Today's Psalm is a reminder of God's promised blessing to those who live to glorify Him. If you have made a commitment to learn to do just that, then this promise is for you. Allow this promise to lead you into a time of prayer and thanksgiving.

Blessed are those who have learned to acclaim You,
who walk in the light of Your presence, O Lord. Psalm 89:15

Yesterday your study revealed why Paul repeatedly reminded the Corinthians that they were God's temple. Very simply stated, because of their own sin and compromise, their "temples" were not reflecting God's glory. Even though Paul recognized them as "those sanctified in Christ Jesus and called to be holy" (1 Corinthians 1:2), they were *not* living holy lives.

You also learned that Paul's concerns and commands applied to a much broader audience far beyond the church at Corinth. In fact, Paul's words hit very close to home because they also apply to *us*. Although many centuries may separate us from the Christians in Corinth, we still struggle with many of the same sins that beset them.

Yet despite our struggles and our sin, Paul (writing under the inspiration of the Holy Spirit) describes us as "temples." What a beautiful metaphor! I'll admit I don't usually feel very much like a temple, and it's certainly not a word I would normally use to describe myself, but (hallelujah!) God does.

Now I think it's time for us to come to a deeper understanding of what it means to be God's temple. As you work through the next several questions, I pray the Lord will give you—and me—a fresh revelation and a new appreciation for His glorious grace toward us.

2. Printed below are the three passages from Corinthians in which Paul describes us as "temples." Please read each passage, and observe carefully what they teach about the temple.

> *Don't you know that you yourselves are God's temple and that God's Spirit lives in you?*
>
> —1 Corinthians 3:16

> *Or do you not know that your body is a temple of the Holy Spirit who is in you, whom you have from God, and that you are not your own? For you have been bought with a price: therefore glorify God in your body.*
>
> —1 Corinthians 6:19–20 *NASB*

> *For we are the temple of the living God. As God has said: "I will live with them and walk among them, and I will be their God, and they will be My people. Therefore come out from them and be separate," says the Lord. "Touch no unclean thing, and I will receive you. I will be a Father to you, and you will be My sons and daughters," says the Lord Almighty. Since we have these promises, dear friends, let us purify ourselves from everything that contaminates body and spirit, perfecting holiness out of reverence for God.*
>
> —2 Corinthians 6:16–7:1

3. Use your own words and words from the passages you just read to record your observations to the following questions:

a. What makes it possible for us to be God's temple?

b. As God's temple, what is our responsibility?

    * Touch no unclean thing

      - Purge unclean

   c.   As God's temple, what is God's promise to us?

4. Please read John 2:13–22, and note what Jesus taught about the temple.

5. Now let's look at another passage from 2 Corinthians where Paul describes us in a little less flattering terms. In the previous scriptures he called our bodies "temples." But in the following passage, he calls us "tents." Please read it, and observe carefully the contrast he makes between our current and future bodies.

> *Now we know that if the earthly tent we live in is destroyed, we have a building from God, an eternal house in heaven, not built by human hands. Meanwhile we groan, longing to be clothed with our heavenly dwelling, because when we are clothed, we will not be found naked. For while we are in this tent, we groan and are burdened, because we do not wish to be unclothed but to be clothed with our heavenly dwelling, so that what is mortal may be swallowed up by life. Now it is God who has made us for this very purpose and has given us the Spirit as a deposit, guaranteeing what is to come. Therefore we are always confident and know that as long as we are at home in the body we are away from the Lord. We live by faith, not by sight. We are confident, I say, and would prefer to be away from the body and at home with the Lord. So we make it our goal to please Him, whether we are at home in the body or away from it.*
>
> —2 Corinthians 5:1–9

6. Using your own words and words from the passage you just read, please record your answers to each of the following questions:

   a.   Describe the primary differences between our "earthly tent" and our future "heavenly dwelling."

b. How has God guaranteed that our mortal body will inherit eternal life?

c. What do you think Paul meant when he said "we groan" (vv. 2, 4) while we are in this earthly "tent" (v. 4)? **NOTE: To answer this question, it may help you to read 2 Corinthians 4:7–11, 16–17.**

d. As long as we inhabit mortal bodies, what should our goal be?

7. There is one final passage I'd like you to see today. It reveals Paul's heartfelt beliefs about his own physical body and life. Please read Philippians 1:19–24, and answer the following questions:

a. According to this passage, what is the supreme purpose of our lives while we are in these physical bodies?

b. How does Paul's perspective about the body differ from the world's perspective about the body?

8. As you compare what you've learned from God's Word today about the body with your own current perspective toward your body, what principles has the Holy Spirit revealed to you that you can apply to your life?

_____

_____

_____

_____

_____

_____

_____

———— ❧ *Day Three* ❧ ————

1. Quiet your heart before the Lord, and spend a few minutes in prayer. Use today's Psalm to express your thanksgiving for the way He has brought you to Himself and has satisfied your every need.

Blessed are those You choose and bring near to live in Your courts! We are filled with the good things of Your house, of Your holy temple. Psalm 65:4

Just imagine. One of these days, we're going to trade in these aging, achy, gravity-prone bodies for perfect, glorified, heavenly bodies. No more wrinkles, no more bifocals, no more diets, no more *exercise* (I do it, but don't *like* it). No more pain, no more sickness, no more death and, best of all, no more sin. One sweet day, we will be liberated from the limits and frailties of these earthly tents—our bodies.

But until then, how are we supposed to live in these mortal, physical bodies? If we follow the world's example, it seems to me we have two primary choices: (1) we can either worship our bodies by constantly focusing on our quest to fit into Size 2 jeans; or (2) we can destroy our bodies by indulging them in addictive, whatever-makes-you-feel-good habits. Neither of those options is good and healthy. But, praise God, there is a much better way.

Today your study will help you gain a biblical perspective about the body. You won't find any miracle diets or wonder drugs, but you will find truth to help you lose many unwanted pounds of worry and self-condemnation. Oh, and you may even get a free facelift—it's called a smile—when you read how much your Creator loves His original, one-of-a-kind creation—*you!*

2. Please read Genesis 1:26–31 and Psalm 139:13–18, and make a list of what you learn from them under the heading below:

   How God Created Me & What He Thinks About His Creation

   a.   Genesis 1:26–31

   b.   Psalm 139:13–18

3. Please read Ephesians 2:10a, and fill in the following blank with the correct word:

   For we are God's _____.

   As I said earlier, our goal is to gain a biblical perspective about our bodies. This word is especially significant for us today, and I think we need to take a closer look at it. The Greek transliteration of this word is *"poiema,"* and it means "a work of art or a masterpiece."[1] But if you look at this Greek word closely, you'll see that there's an English word contained within it. It's the word "poem." Isn't that beautiful! And when you put all of this information together, this verse is actually saying: "For we are God's poem, God's masterpiece, God's work of art." I don't know how that makes you feel, but I definitely think you need to put down your pen for a minute and bow your head to let this truth sink deep into your heart. I'm going to do the same thing—and I'm going to need a tissue for these tears that are running down my cheeks.

4. Now let's take a look at some scriptures that will give us a biblical perspective about the body. Please read the following verses and then make a list of what you learn from them under the heading below:

   A Biblical Perspective of the Body

   a.   Matthew 26:41

   b.   Luke 12:22–31 (Although the primary context of this passage concerns worry and covetousness, there also are some very applicable principles regarding the body and biblical priorities.)

   c.   Romans 12:1–2

5. Does the Bible have anything to say about diet and exercise? Because it's such a practical, relevant book—yes, it does. Fad diets will come and go, but God's Word has stood the test of time in every subject it addresses—even food. Please read the following scriptures, and record any principles and insights you gain from them regarding diet and exercise:

    a.   Proverbs 23:20–21

    b.   Proverbs 25:16

    c.   Romans 14:14–17, 21–23

    d.   1 Corinthians 9:23–27

    e.   1 Corinthians 10:31

    f.   1 Timothy 4:7–8

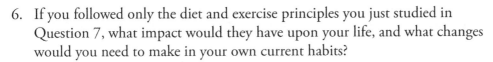

"What does the
bible say about
healthy living?." Book

6. If you followed only the diet and exercise principles you just studied in Question 7, what impact would they have upon your life, and what changes would you need to make in your own current habits?

7. Beauty is big business in today's world. What does the Bible say about physical beauty? Please read the following verses and record what you learn:

   a.   1 Samuel 16:7

   b.   Proverbs 31:30

   c.   Isaiah 53:2 (This is a prophecy about Jesus. Please note what you learn about His appearance, and how it might have affected Him had His incarnation and earthly ministry occurred in our day.)

   d.   1 Peter 3:3–4

8. According to the scriptures you just read in Question 9, what kind of beauty does God value?

9. As you've studied the scriptures today, how has the Holy Spirit spoken to you? How will you respond to what He's revealed to you? Please briefly journal your answers to these questions.

_____

_____

_____

_____

_____

_____

_____

꧁ Day Four ꧂

1. In light of what we're about to study, today's Psalm is especially appropriate. After you've read this passage, prayerfully commit to live the way He would have you live, to do the things He would have you do, and to speak the words He would have you say.

> *Lord, who may dwell in Your sanctuary?*
> *Who may live on Your holy hill?*
> *He whose walk is blameless and who does what is righteous,*
> *who speaks the truth from his heart.* Psalm 15:1-2

In Day One of your homework, you discovered why Paul repeatedly reminded the Corinthians that their bodies were the temple of God. Although Paul affirmed them as believers, he called them to account in the areas of personal purity and holiness. He was teaching them that their spiritual relationship with Christ should affect every other area of their lives.

In today's culture, if someone professes their belief in certain moral values and fails to practice them, they're described as someone who is able to "compartmentalize their life." And while such a description may sound sophisticated and even somewhat enlightened, Scripture has another term for this type of behavior. Scripture calls it plain, ol' "hypocrisy."

God's Word consistently calls us to live consistent lives. Our beliefs should parallel the way we live. The God we profess to possess is holy, righteous and pure. The only way we can glorify Him is by living holy, righteous and pure lives. We cannot glorify God by compartmentalizing our spiritual lives apart from our physical lives.

God's standards for His children are high; and when I look at my own fleshly abilities, I get disheartened by my weaknesses, shortcomings, and downright failures. But when I focus on Him and all that He's given me through the power of His indwelling Spirit, I am reminded, encouraged and confident that "He who began a good work in (me) will carry it on to completion until the day of Christ Jesus" (Philippians 1:6). How grateful I am for the promise of His Word!

Today we will be studying God's standard for our lives. As you study these standards, please do not be dismayed by your own shortcomings. Instead remember what you learned yesterday from Ephesians 2:10. You are God's *poiema*, and the Divine Poet is passionately devoted to completing and perfecting you, His beloved poem.

2. For a clear, concise understanding of God's standard for our lives, please read the following scriptures and briefly record what they teach.

    a. Ephesians 1:4

    b. 1 Thessalonians 4:7

3. *The Complete Word Study Dictionary New Testament* defines the word "holy" as "separation, consecration, devotion to the service of Deity, sharing in God's purity and abstaining from earth's defilement."[2] This is a very high standard, and it may seem unachievable until we look at the wonderful hope God has given us in His Word. Please read 1 Peter 2:24, and record how God has made it possible for us to attain His holy standard:

4. We've seen God's standard and how it is attained. Now it's time to see our responsibility as individual believers in light of all that He's done for us. Ephesians 1–3 describes what Christ has done for us through His gracious work of redemption. Ephesians 4–6 describes how we should live as a result of Christ's redemption. I have divided Ephesians 4–6 into five separate categories, and each of these categories is listed below. Please read the scriptures listed under each category. Then number and compile a list of the instructions and principles regarding personal holiness that you find in these passages. I've begun each of these lists just to help you get started.

How to Live in a Worthy Manner
Ephesians 4:1–3, 11–16

1. *v. 2 By being humble, gentle, patient and loving with others.*

_____

_____

_____

_____

_____

_____

Do Not Live Like The Lost
Ephesians 4:17–32

1. *v 17 By being vain and empty in my thought life.*

_____

_____

_____

_____

_____

_____

Live By Imitating God
Ephesians 5:1–7

1. *v. 8 By sacrificially loving others and loving God.*

_____

_____

_____

_____

_____

_____

Live as Children of Light
Ephesians 5:8–14

1. *v. 9 In goodness, righteousness and truth.*

_____

_____

_____

_____

_____

_____

Live Wisely
Ephesians 5:15–21

1. *v. 16 Making the hours of my day count for eternity.*

_____

_____

_____

_____

_____

_____

5. Because of the lists you've just completed, you now have a very clear picture of what holy living looks like. Now it's time for some very practical application.

a. Prayerfully review your lists again, and ask the Holy Spirit to pinpoint any areas of sin and compromise in your life. Please briefly list anything He reveals to you.

b. If the Holy Spirit has convicted you of any specific sin, please open your Bible to Psalm 51:1–12. Use David's prayer as your own as you confess before the Lord the sin He has revealed to you. Allow the Lord to cleanse and purify you completely. Renew your commitment to be holy even as He is holy.

    c.   Confession of sin should always be followed by repentance from sin. In what way is God calling you to change and turn away from your sin? How will you respond?

6. As you consider what you've studied this week about the body, I want to ask you a few questions. Briefly record your thoughts to each question:

    a.   Why do you think Paul uses the words "temple" and "tent" to describe our bodies?

    b.   When he refers to the body as a "temple," what do you think he is emphasizing?

    c.   When he refers to the body as a "tent," what do you think he is emphasizing?

    d.   What do you think Paul is trying to teach us about our bodies?

7. As we close today's lesson, I want to give you a very encouraging passage of scripture. Please read it, and write a prayer of praise to God for the promise these scriptures contain.

> *Grace and peace be yours in abundance through the knowledge of God and of Jesus our Lord. His divine power has given us everything we need for life and godliness through our knowledge of Him who called us by His own glory and goodness.*
>
> —2 Peter 1:2–3

_____

_____

_____

_____

_____

_____

_____

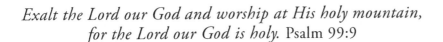 *Day Five*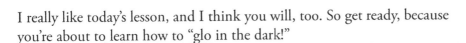

1. Bow your head as you begin your time of study today, and let today's Psalm guide you as you praise and worship your holy God.

> *Exalt the Lord our God and worship at His holy mountain, for the Lord our God is holy.* Psalm 99:9

I really like today's lesson, and I think you will, too. So get ready, because you're about to learn how to "glo in the dark!"

2. Begin your study by reviewing a passage you studied yesterday, Ephesians 5:8–9, then answer the following questions:

a. Describe your life before and after you became a Christian (v. 8).

b. How is light manifested through your daily life (v. 9)?

3. Let's discover more about this light you possess. Please read the following scriptures, and record what you learn from them about the light you've been given:

a. John 1:4–5—Who is the source of our light?

b. John 8:12—What is the promise to those who have light?

c. Matthew 5:14–16—What are we commanded to do with this light?

d. Matthew 5:16—How will others be able to see our light?

e. Matthew 5:16—What is the most important reason and result of letting our light shine ?

4. I think one of the best examples of someone who truly "glowed in the dark" is the prophet Daniel. Daniel was a young Jewish man when he was taken into Babylonian captivity in the year 605 B.C. The nation of Babylon was idolatrous and wicked, and Daniel's faith was tested many times as he served several of Babylon's pagan kings. Please read the following three accounts about Daniel, and note how Daniel "glowed in the dark" by letting his light shine:

    a. Daniel 1

    b. Daniel 5:1–17, 26–31 (Note how Daniel is described in vv. 11–14.)

    c. Daniel 6 (Note how Daniel is described in vv. 3–4.)

5. How did Daniel's life reveal the light of God's glory to the culture in which he lived, and how did his example inspire and encourage you?

Nov 7th - week 3

6. You've done a great deal of study this past week, and I trust the Lord has used His Word to transform and to renew your mind. Reflect upon what He has revealed to you and the way you see Him working in your life, then journal your thoughts by completing the sentences provided on the following journal page.

My Journal

THIS WEEK THE LORD...

_____

_____

_____

_____

_____

_____

_____

_____

AS A RESULT, I...

_____

_____

_____

_____

_____

_____

_____

_____

_____

I hope you've seen this week that God is very interested in your physical body. But His primary interest doesn't have much to do with your dress size or with your outward appearance. God isn't "in" to perfect bodies. God is "in" to holy bodies.

But just think—one of these days no more "cottage cheese" thighs, no more jiggly arms, and no more "chicken skin" necks. Until the day God gives you a glorious, glorified body, you just keep letting His light shine through the "tent" He's given you. That's right—*you glo, girl!*

The Temple: SHINE! REFLECTING GOD'S GLORY

Or do you not know that your body is a temple of the Holy Spirit who is in you, whom you have from God, and that you are not your own? For you have been bought with a price: therefore glorify God in your body.

—1 Corinthians 6:19–20 *NASB*

World's Philosophy: My body is __my__ __temple__.

Biblical Philosophy: My body is __Gods__ __temple__.

Key Principle: We glorify God in our everyday lives by reflecting God's glory through __pure__ and __holy__ living.

One of the Hebrew words for glory is __hala__ = * to __shine__

* to give _____

__Hala__ is the root word for __halle__ = giving glory to God.[3]

Ephes 1:4

Question: How can we "__shine__"/__reflect__ God's glory?

Answer: By living __holy__ and __pure__ lives. *Ephesians 1:4, 2:19–21*

Question: What does a __pure__ and __holy__ __lifestyle__ look like?

Answer: It doesn't look like the "__old__ __you__." *Ephesians 4:17–22*

* caught up in a __futile__, vain mindset

* no __spiritual__ understanding

* given over to __sensuality__ and impurity

* continual lust for __more__

It does look like the "__new__ __you__." *Ephesians 4:24*

* like __God__ = godly

* righteous

* __holy__

In your relationships with others, it looks like:

Ephesians 4:25–27

* being ___truthful___

* being ___angry___ but not ___sinning___

* seeking speedy ___restoration___

In your words and attitudes, it sounds like:

Ephesians 4:29–32

* words that ___build___, bless and ___benefit___

* kindness and ___compassion___

* ___unconditional___ forgiveness

In your personal morality, it looks like:

Ephesians 5:3–5

* not even a ___hint___ of sexual immorality

* not even a hint of impurity or ___greed___

* not even a hint of foul or ___coarse___ language

In your workplace, it looks like:

Ephesians 4:28

* being honest and not ___steal___

* being ___hardworking___

* ___sharing___ with others

In your service to God and others, it looks like:

Ephesians 5:1–2

* ___loving___ as Christ loved

* ___giving___ as Christ gave

* unconditional, ___sacrificial___ love

In your partnerships with others, it looks like:

Ephesians 5:6–7

* not being ___deceived___ by empty words

* not being ___partners___ with unbelievers
  - contracts
  - partnership

Question: Why should you live a holy and pure lifestyle? *Ephesians 5:8*

Answer: Because you've ___received___ the ___light___ of Christ, and you're called to let His ___light___ ___shine___ through your life.

* Proverbs 4:18 *

Final Exhortation:

Give up ___physical___ ___perfection___,

and become, instead, ___Gods___ ___reflection___!

The Temple: DETAILS...DETAILS...DETAILS!

On the Ideal Saturday Morning, the alarm clock does not ring. It does not ring because it was not set the previous night. It was not set the previous night because there are no early morning appointments on the calendar. And since there are no early morning appointments on the calendar, this means . . . I can *get* up . . . whenever I *wake* up. *Ahhhh*, now that's what I call the beginning of an ideal Saturday.

Upon waking, the agenda for the Ideal Saturday Morning includes an hour or so of uninterrupted down time, sitting at the breakfast table, wearing my favorite robe, enjoying a hot mug of coffee, blissfully reading the Saturday morning newspaper. Sounds like quite a magnificent agenda to me.

As I write this introduction, it's Saturday afternoon, and I'm reflecting upon what almost was an Ideal Saturday Morning. Things were going so well. There were no alarms, no appointments, the house was still quiet, I was wearing my comfy robe, and I was enjoying a lovely cup of coffee as I read the paper. Only one thing prevented me from experiencing a sublimely satisfying Saturday morning. That one thing was one section of the newspaper.

Every week my Saturday newspaper includes a separate section entitled "religion," and every week I unfold that section and scan its headlines. Years ago I would optimistically open it expecting to find it full of inspiring, edifying reading. But through the years I have become much less optimistic about what to expect from the religion section. I now realize this section includes only what its title claims: a collection of articles and features about *religion.*

As you can see, I'm no longer naïve. I do not have unrealistic expectations of the Saturday religion section. Even so, today's edition sabotaged my Ideal Saturday Morning. Before I could even read the headlines, my eyes were instantly drawn to a picture of someone I never under any circumstances would have expected to see on the religion page. It was Madonna. That's right, Madonna, the rock star. Madonna was the "cover girl" for the Saturday religion page.

Lest you think that the sight of Madonna's picture on the religion page was what upset my practically perfect morning, please allow me to explain. You see, it wasn't the inclusion of her photo on the religion page that bothered me; it was the article accompanying the picture that broke my heart and blew away the bliss of my Ideal Saturday Morning.

The article explained how Madonna has embraced the religion of kaballah, a form of Jewish mysticism. Shunning her former "Material Girl" persona, she has morphed into the new-age "Spiritual Girl." Through her current Reinvention World Tour, her music videos, and in dozens of interviews with the media, Madonna is now overtly marketing the false teaching of the kaballah—and thousands of her young fans are certain to be converted. As I read the article, my heart began to ache with grief.

THIS WEEK'S KEY PRINCIPLE:

We glorify God in our everyday lives by giving Him authority over every detail in our lives.

The Temple

DETAILS...DETAILS...DETAILS!

Magnifying my grief was another article on the religion page entitled *"The Science of the Soul: East Meets West as Deepak Chopra Offers Listeners Tools for Spiritual Enlightenment."* [1] Deepak Chopra is someone very few people knew anything about until he appeared on *Oprah* several years ago. Since that appearance, his books have become best-sellers, and he has become one of America's most popular new age gurus of eastern mysticism.

Chopra himself says,

> The basis of everything that I write is that if you understand consciousness and how consciousness becomes physical reality, then you'll understand everything from perception to emotions and moods and relationships and environments and social interactions and, ultimately, the intelligence that is at the heart of the universe. [2]

Even if I read Chopra's words a hundred times, I doubt they'd ever make much sense to me. Yet millions are following his teaching hoping it will eventually enable them to know God. But eastern religion will not produce a true knowledge of God. Are you beginning to see now why my heart was so distressed and why my Ideal Saturday Morning was now undone?

Within the heart of every single one of us is the desire to know our Creator. God Himself implanted that desire. He *wants* us to *want* to know Him. And from the beginning of creation, God has made Himself known. He has not concealed Himself from His creation. He has not masked Himself in mysticism. He is not veiled within the kaballah, and He is not attained by achieving a higher degree of consciousness. In fact, God wants the world to know Him so much that He sent "His one and only Son...into the world...to save the world" (John 3:16–17). God has done everything possible in order that we may know Him. But the truth is: "Light has come into the world, but men loved darkness instead of light" (John 3:19). I think that verse is especially true here in America. God has given us countless opportunities to know Him through the light of His Son, through the light of His Word, and through the light of His reflection in the lives of His children. But many still prefer darkness.

After I finished reading the religion section, I seriously began rethinking the Ideal Saturday Morning scenario. Maybe I should just exclude the religion section from the agenda. After all, it's depressing and even heartbreaking at times. But as I pondered that possible solution, the Lord spoke to me: "Your heart needs to be broken. Your heart needs to be grieved. You need to be reminded that you do not live in an Ideal World." As I meditated further upon what the Lord was telling me, His message became very clear: the only true and lasting cure for the darkness in our world today is the light of Jesus Christ.

Therefore, despite the fact that my Ideal Saturday Morning was derailed and disrupted today, the result is that I'm now more committed than ever before to allowing the glorious light of Christ to shine through my everyday life. And now that I think about it, maybe I really did experience the Ideal Saturday Morning after all.

1. Let today's Psalm lead you into God's glorious presence as you draw near to Him in prayer. Praise Him for allowing you to come before Him in confidence because of the work of His Son, your Savior.

> *I long to dwell in Your tent forever,*
> *and take refuge in the shelter of Your wings.* Psalm 61:4

2. By now I hope you have just about committed the key verses for this study to memory. As you can see, these verses are partially printed below. Please fill in the blanks from memory to complete these verses. Then practice quoting this passage aloud several times until you are able to quote it with ease from memory.

> *Or do you not* <u>Know</u> *that your* <u>body</u> *is a* <u>temple</u>
> *of the* <u>Holy</u> <u>Spirit</u> *who is* <u>in</u> <u>you</u>, *whom you have*
> *from* <u>God</u>, *and that you are* <u>not</u> <u>your</u> <u>own</u>?
> *For you have been* <u>bought</u> <u>at</u> <u>a</u> <u>price</u>:
> *therefore* <u>glorify</u> <u>God</u> <u>in</u> <u>your</u> <u>body</u>.
> —1 Corinthians 6:19–20 *NASB*

The truths contained in these verses are vital and practical. They remind us about who we are, whose we are, and the high calling God has placed upon our lives. Because He purchased us through the blood of His Son and now resides within us through the power of His indwelling Spirit, we are called—and equipped—to glorify God in our bodies.

3. By way of review, what term does Paul use to describe our bodies in 1 Corinthians 3:16, 6:19–20, and 2 Corinthians 6:16? <u>temple</u>

4. In 2 Corinthians 6:16, Paul quotes several Old Testament references to explain how and why we are God's temple. These scriptures are printed for you below. As you read them, underline the repeated and similar quote within each passage.

> *What agreement is there between the temple of God and idols? For we are the temple of the living God. As God has said: "<u>I will live with them and walk among them</u>, and I will be their God, and they will be My people."*
> —2 Corinthians 6:16

> *So I will consecrate the Tent of Meeting and the altar and will consecrate Aaron and his sons to serve Me as priests. Then I will <u>dwell among the Israelites and be their God</u>.*
> —Exodus 29:44-45

I will put My dwelling place among you, and I will not abhor you. <u>I will walk among you and be your God, and you will be My people.</u>

—Leviticus 26:11–12

These passages from Exodus and Leviticus are God's promises to Moses, and they refer to the Old Covenant tabernacle. Therefore, in 2 Corinthians 6:16, Paul is paralleling the New Covenant temple—the individual Christian and the corporate church—with the Old Covenant tabernacle. He is also revealing their *most important common trait: God's presence within them.*

While the Old Covenant law was superseded by the New Covenant of grace through Jesus Christ (Hebrews 7–10), there remain many principles and parallels in the Old Covenant that give us a greater understanding about how we can worship and glorify God. In other words, the lessons and symbolism from the Old Covenant continue to have application for the New Covenant believer. While we do not live under the rules and commands of the Old Covenant laws, we can still learn a great deal about God and our relationship with Him as we study Old Covenant worship. The Old Covenant is rich in symbolism which was fulfilled in Christ, the New Covenant Christian, the New Testament church and, ultimately, in heaven.

For the next several weeks, we will be learning some very practical principles we can apply to our lives as we seek to glorify God. Our study will span many years of Old Testament history. We'll watch God teach His chosen people how to please and glorify Him through the sacrificial system of worship practiced at the tabernacle and, later, at the temple.

In my own personal walk with the Lord, I have experienced enormous blessings and benefits from studying the tabernacle and the temple; and that's what I hope you will gain and more as you begin your study of the tabernacle today.

5. This week you will be reading extensively from Exodus as you do your homework and I will be asking you to mark several key phrases in your Bibles. **NOTE: In order to identify this <u>key phrase</u>, it is very important that you use one of the following Bible translations as you do this week's homework (the key phrase is not as clearly evident in other translations):**

    *   New American Standard
    *   New King James Version
    *   King James Version

Please read Exodus 19:1–8, and answer the following questions:

a. According to verses 5–6, what did God require of the Israelites in order for them to be in covenant with Him?

Obey His voice and keep His covenant.

b. How did the people respond to God's requirement regarding the covenant (vv. 7–8)?

They said they would do all that the Lord had spoken

6. Please quickly scan (you do not need to thoroughly read each verse) Exodus chapters 20–23, and summarize briefly what these chapters contain.

10 commandments, Gods rules and promises Examples of situations, and how to respond to them.

7. Please read Exodus 24:3–8, then answer the following questions:

a. What did Moses do when he descended from the mountain?

Wrote all the words of the Lord, built an alter at the foot of the mountain, and 12 pillars according to the 12 tribes of Israel

b. What part of these ordinances and laws did the Israelites agree to keep? Please circle one:

Some   Certain parts of it   (All)

c. What does their response reveal about their desire and their own belief in themselves?

Desire to be 100% w/ God.
Belief that they could keep all of the laws and oridances

d. How was this covenant instituted and sealed (vv. 5–8)?

* Moses took half the blood and put it in basins, half sprinkled on the alter.
* Read the Book of the covenant
* Took the blood, sprinkled it on the people

8. As you may already know, it won't take long for the Israelites to break their vow of obedience to God. But I want you to ponder this question: How are we often just like the Israelites? Please record your honest insights.

    We tend to promise a lot to God, but do not follow through.

Day Two

1. Begin your time of study today by praising God for His presence and for His light in your life. Commit to live and walk in the light He has given you.

    Blessed are those who have learned to acclaim You,
    who walk in the light of Your presence, O Lord. Psalm 89:15

    Yesterday we began studying Exodus and God's covenant with Moses and the Israelites. Today we will continue reading and observing Exodus. As you complete today's homework, I'm praying you'll discover anew God's love for you.

2. Please read Exodus 24:12–18, and answer the following questions:

    a. Why did God call Moses to come up on the mountain?

    To give him a tablet of stone, and the law + commandments

    b. What happened on the mountain when Moses went up?

    A cloud covered the mountain

    c. What did the Israelites see?

    Consuming fire on the top of the mountain

    d. How long was Moses on the mountain with God?

    40 days and 40 nights

3. Please read Exodus 25:1–9, and answer the following questions:

    a. According to verse 2, what were the Israelites commanded to do?

        Bring God an offering

    b. What were the Israelites commanded to do with the contribution and why (v. 8)?

        Make God a sanctuary, that He may dwell among them

    c. What does this reveal about God?

        He wants to be w/ the children of Israel, but only if they want to as well "willingly with his heart" vs 2

    d. What does this reveal to us about our greatest need?

        Quality time with the Lord, a place for worship and communion.

    e. How were the Israelites specifically told to construct God's sanctuary (v. 9)?

        According to all that God shows them, the pattern of the tabernacle, all its furnishing.

4. In Exodus 25:10, God begins giving the blueprint for the construction of His earthly sanctuary, the tabernacle. The tabernacle will be inhabited by the very presence of God. It will illustrate how sinful man can draw near to and find forgiveness from a holy God. Let's review for a moment the *order* of what we've seen since we began studying Exodus yesterday:

    *   Exodus 19:1–7—God offers to enter into a covenant with the Israelites if they will agree to obey Him.

    *   Exodus 19:8—The Israelites agree to obey God.

    *   Exodus 20–23—Moses meets with God and receives the Ten Commandments and the additional laws and ordinances of the covenant.

    *   Exodus 24:1–8—Moses recounts the laws of the covenant to the Israelites, they vow to keep them, and they enter into a blood covenant with God.

    *   Exodus 25:1–12—God commands the Israelites to make a sanctuary so He can dwell among them.

The Temple

Based upon this review, please circle your answers to the following questions:

a. Have the Israelites sinned and broken the covenant yet?

Yes   (No)

b. Will they soon forsake God and break this covenant (to confirm your answer to this question, please review Exodus 32:1–4)?

(Yes)   No

At this point, we need to stop for a moment to consider something quite marvelous. God is omniscient, which means He possesses full knowledge of all things past, present, and *future*. Yet in Exodus, God initiates a covenant with Israel and makes plans to dwell among them even though He *knows* they are about to betray Him.

Now to enable you to see things from God's perspective, let me give you a couple of questions to ponder: (1) Would you initiate a covenant with someone if you knew with certainty they would betray you? (2) Would you make plans to be intimate with someone if you knew they'd forsake you and turn their back on you?

5. As you consider what you have just read, what does this reveal to you about God and His character?

God is an awesome God. He loves us, and wants us to experience His love

6. In Exodus 25:10–26:37, God begins giving Moses the instructions for building the tabernacle. As you quickly scan these chapters (you do not need to thoroughly read each verse), please do the following:

a. Look for a key repeated phrase woven throughout these chapters, and underline it in your Bible each time you see it. **NOTE: You must use one of the Bible translations recommended from Day One, Question 5 in order to discover this key repeated phrase.**

b. Quickly scan chapters 25–26 again. As you're scanning, compile a brief list of the major and minor details included in the instructions for the tabernacle. **NOTE: Relax. There are no right or wrong answers for this list. Simply include what you believe are some of the major and minor details regarding the tabernacle (its furnishings, contents, materials, etc).** To help you get started, I've begun these lists for you.

Major Details	*Minor Details*
1. 25:10 ark of acacia wood	1. 26:4 loops on curtains
2. 25:13 poles of acacia wood	2.
3.	3.
4.	4.
5.	5.
6.	6.
7.	7.
8.	8.
9.	9.
10.	10

7. What repeated command do you see in Exodus 25:9, 40, and what principle is God reinforcing to Moses by repeating it?

According to the pattern which was shown God is giving Moses precise directions. He wants him to be accurate.

8. What truths and principles have you learned today that you can apply to your own life?

God is focused on the details of our lives! He wants to be involved in all of it, the big and small matters of our life. I must let God play a role in all aspects of my life.

DETAILS...DETAILS...DETAILS!

— Days Three & Four —

1. One of the ways we glorify God is by radiating the joy He's given us. Do you need a fresh infusion of His joy today? Sister, I need a fresh dose of His joy daily, and I find it in His presence. Let today's Psalm remind you of the wonderful gifts God has given you—eternal life, eternal joy, and eternal pleasures—because of His constant presence in your life. Spend some time in prayer thanking Him for these gifts, and ask Him today for a fresh infilling of joy.

> *You have made known to me the path of life;*
> *You will fill me with joy in Your presence,*
> *with eternal pleasures at Your right hand.* Psalm 16:11

Today and tomorrow you will continue to study God's instructions to Moses regarding the tabernacle. Please do part of the following homework today, and complete the rest of it tomorrow. Happy studying!

2. Please quickly scan Exodus 27–30, and as you scan:

   a. Look for the same key repeated phrase woven throughout these chapters that you saw in yesterday's reading, and underline it in your Bible each time you see it. It is the most repeated phrase in this entire section that we are studying in Exodus. **NOTE: You must use one of the Bible translations recommended from Day One, Question 5 to clearly identify this key repeated phrase.**

   b. Make a brief list of some of the major and minor details included in these instructions on the lists below, just as you did in yesterday's homework. **NOTE: Remember, just like yesterday's list, there are no right or wrong answers for this assignment; simply include what you believe are some of the major and minor details regarding the tabernacle (its furnishings, contents, materials, etc).** Again, I've begun these lists for you to help you get started.

Major Details	Minor Details
1. 27:1 altar of acacia wood	1. 27:1 sockets of bronze
2. 27:2 Horns on its 4 corners	2. 27:3 all utensils of bronze
3. 27:6 Poles for the alter	3. 27:17 bands of silver and bronze sockets
4. 27:9 Court of the tabernacle	4. 27:20 pure oil of pressed olives
5. 27:10 Twenty pillars	5. 28:22 Chains for breast plate
6. 28:15 Breast plate of judgment.	6. 28:23 Two rings of gold
7. 28:21 Stones names of sons of Israel	7. 28:33 pomegranates of blue, purple, & scarlet
8. 28:31 robe of ephod all blue	8. 28:34 golden bell & pomegranate
9. 28:36 Pure gold plate	9. 28:42 Linen trousers
10. 29:6 Turban on Aarons head	10.

3. Please quickly scan chapters 28–29, and make notes regarding the various ways the priests were set apart by God.

- Holy garments were to be made for them,

  - purple, gold, blue, and scarlet thread, fine linen Ex 28:6

- Gird them w/ sashes,

- Turban on his (Aaron) head, and put holy crown on the turban Ex 29:6

4. Please read the verses on the following chart, and note what you learn about the Old and New Covenant priesthood. Also note the contrasts and comparisons you see between them.

Old Covenant Priesthood	New Covenant Priesthood	Contrasts and Comparisons
Ex. 28:1	1 Peter 2:5, 9	
Ex. 29:20–21	1 Peter 1:2, 18–19	

5. I love what the New International Version of the Bible says about the garments of the priests. It says these garments gave them "dignity and honor...so that they may serve (God) as priests" (Exodus 28:2–4). The New Living Translation of the Bible says it this way:

    Make special clothing for Aaron to show his separation to God— beautiful garments that will lend dignity to his work. Instruct all those who have special skills as tailors to make the garments that will set Aaron apart from everyone else, so he may serve Me as a priest.

    —Exodus 28:2–3 *NLT*

    The priestly clothing set the priests apart and signified the holiness, dignity and honor befitting one called by God to be a priest.

    God has also called us to be holy and to be priests (1 Peter 1:15, 2:5). As such, our clothing should reflect holiness, dignity and honor—which isn't exactly the usual fare of most fashion shows these days! Forget *Vogue* and the trends today's "fashionistas" tout; let's get our fashion statement straight from God's Word. Please read the verses on the following chart, and make a list in your own words of what the Bible teaches about fashion and style:

Fashion Do's & Don'ts for the Well-Dressed Woman of God:

Proverbs 31:22, 25
Matthew 6:25, 28, 30
John 13:3–5, 14–16 (What did Jesus' "attire" in these verses symbolize, and how can we emulate His example?)
Colossians 3:12–14
1 Timothy 2:9–10
1 Peter 3:3–4
1 Peter 5:5

6. As you review your "Fashion Do's and Don'ts" list, what specific "do's" and "don'ts" do you need to add to, or subtract from, your life and wardrobe in order to be well-dressed according to God's standards? Compile your insights on the following lists:

Fashion Do's To Add   *Fashion Don'ts To Subtract*

——————————————— ———————————————

——————————————— ———————————————

——————————————— ———————————————

——————————————— ———————————————

——————————————— ———————————————

7. Using the insights the Holy Spirit has given you during these two days of study, write out a prayer expressing your desire to be set apart unto God so that you may serve Him in holiness.

_____

_____

_____

_____

_____

_____

_____

— ❧ *Day Five* ❧ —

1. I hope one of the things you've become more grateful for this week is the blessing that you're no longer under the Old Covenant! Aren't you thankful for Jesus' work on the cross and for the glorious indwelling of His presence within us? As you begin your final day of study this week, express your gratitude and thankfulness to God in prayer.

Great is the Lord, and most worthy of praise.
Psalm 48:1

2. For the past several days, you've been reading God's instructions to Moses regarding the tabernacle—and you've done a *lot* of reading. I want to help you today by giving you a synopsis of Exodus 31–38. You've already read Exodus 24–30, so the following will begin with Exodus 31:

   • Exodus 31—God chooses Bezelel, a gifted craftsman from the tribe of Judah to oversee the construction of the tabernacle, the furnishings, and the priestly garments. God gives Moses the two stone tablets of the Law.

   • Exodus 32—Moses descends from Mt. Sinai and finds the people worshipping a golden calf. In anger, he shatters the two stone tablets.

   • Exodus 33—Moses meets with God and asks to see God's glory.

   • Exodus 34—Moses ascends Mt. Sinai with two blank, stone tablets. Moses sees God's glory. God renews His covenant with Moses and the Israelites and writes the Ten Commandments upon the stone tablets. Moses descends the mountain with his face aglow.

   • Exodus 35–38—These chapters include the details of the actual construction of the tabernacle.

3. Today please read Exodus 39–40. In these chapters you'll observe how the Israelites responded to God's instructions regarding the tabernacle. Personally, I love these chapters and the way they conclude the book of Exodus in a beautiful, powerful way. As you read:

   a. Feel free to use any of the Bible translations previously recommended (see Day One, Question 5) or you may use the New International Version if you like.

   b. Look for a new key repeated phrase woven throughout these two chapters.

4. As you have read Exodus this week, you have observed two key repeated phrases from Exodus 25–30 and 39–40. These key phrases are recorded for you below using the New American Standard Bible *(NASB)*, the New King James Version *(NKJV)*, the King James Version *(KJV)*, and the New International Version *(NIV)*:

   a. Key repeated phrase from Exodus 25–30:

      NASB and NKJV—"you shall"

      KJV—"thou shalt"

      NOTE: This phrase is repeated over 100 times in these chapters.

   b. Key repeated phrase from Exodus 39–40:

      NASB—"just as the Lord had commanded Moses"

      NKJV, KJV, NIV—"as the Lord commanded Moses"

      NOTE: This phrase is repeated 18 times in these chapters. You may want to underline these, also.

5. Think about it: how are these two key repeated phrases connected? Please record your insights.

6. Over the past several days, you have made lists of some of the major and minor details God included in His instructions regarding the tabernacle. Record your insights to the following questions:

   a. How do you think God views details?

   b. How fully did the Israelites carry out these details?

   c. According to Exodus 40:34–38, what was the result of their obedience and attention to detail?

7. Record your insights to the following questions:

   a. How do you think God would have responded if they had done their own thing in constructing the tabernacle, or had added to or subtracted from God's blueprint and instructions?

   b. What application does this have for us today?

8. You've seen that God is very interested in details. And the only way to glorify Him fully is by surrendering every detail of your life—the major and the minor ones—to Him. Put down your pen. Put down this workbook. Now spend a few moments in His presence and ask Him this question:

Father, what details in my life do I need to surrender to You right now?

After you've given Him time to speak to your heart, you'll definitely want to record what He reveals to you.

_____

_____

_____

_____

_____

_____

_____

_____

_____

_____

⟨decorative flourish⟩

At the conclusion of last week's lesson, we pondered the glory of our heavenly, glorified bodies. This week ponder with me (humorously if you will—it's been a serious week of study, and we need a little laughter) about our heavenly wardrobe. One day we will no longer have to even think about what we'll wear. And I just have to tell you, I love God's choice for our eternal attire—robes!

If you are a robe lover like I am (I confess to having a genuine affection for my wardrobe of robes—especially my soft, pastel pink chenille robe that zips up the front), you are just going to love heaven! You'll be wearing your favorite fashion statement every day with absolutely no worry about receiving a citation from the fashion police (or from your husband or teenagers for that matter)! In fact, my dear, you'll be right in style, you'll be wearing the latest fashion, and you'll look simply glorious.

If you're not a robe lover, please disregard the rest of this. It may be more than you can bear. But if you're like me, and you're looking forward to that day when we'll be able to wear our robes all day every day, I've got a great cheer we robe lovers can chant until then:

Robes in heaven,

24/7!!

Dear sister (whether you're a robe lover or not), in all of the ordinary details of your everyday life, may His indwelling presence be evident to everyone whose life you touch. Keep gloing, girl!

The Temple: THE GOD OF EVERY DETAIL

[handwritten: Surrender every detail to God.]

Key Principle: *We glorify God in our everyday lives by giving Him authority over every detail in our lives.*

I. Why was the Old Covenant/ __The law__ even __neccesary__ ?

God used it to:

A. __Reveal__ Himself and His __character__ to them. Deut. 5:1–16

B. Instruct them how to obey Him and how to __reflect__ His holy __character__. Deut. 7:6, 9

C. __Set__ them __apart__ from all other __people__ *[handwritten above: nations]*. Deut. 7:6

D. __Reveal__ to them that they were __sinners__. Gal. 3:19,22

E. _____ and to _____ them until Christ came. Gal. 3:23–24

II. What other principles did the Old Covenant __reveal__ ?

A. Questions to Review: Exodus 24:12–30:8

1. Why did God call Moses up to Mt. Sinai? __Stone tablets, give Moses the law__

2. What were the Israelites told to construct? __A sanctuary for God__

3. Why were they to construct it? __So that God may dwell w/them__

4. How were they to construct it? __According to everywhere detail__

5. What key repeated phrase is found in Ex. 25:10–30? __"you shall"__

B. Principles About God:

1. God __loves__ us, and He longs to __dwell__ __among__ us.

2. God will dwell among us and have fellowship with us __on His terms__.

3. God is a God of __details__, and __details__ matter to God.

C. Questions to Review: Exodus 39–40

1. What key repeated phrase is found in Exodus 39–40? __Just as the Lord has commanded Moses__

2. How did the Israelites construct the tabernacle (39:42–43)? __They did all the work just as God commanded__

3. What was the result of their obedience to God (40:34–35)? __the glory of God filled the tabernacle__

D. Principles About God:

1. God will __reveal__ the details He __requires__ of us—where He requires _____ and __repentance__ in our lives, He'll reveal it.

2. God will not require us to do anything He will not __equip__ and __enable__ us to do.

3. God will __fill__ our lives with His glory and will enable us to glorify Him as we __surrender__ __every__ __detail__ of our lives to Him.

[handwritten bottom: Show me any details of my life, I need to surrender to You.]

[handwritten bottom right: Psalm 27:23]

The Temple: SYMBOLS THAT STILL SPEAK

Sometimes it seems like the God of the Old Testament is somehow… well…*different* from the God of the New Testament. In reading the Old Testament accounts of the flood, the plagues of Egypt, and God's punishment upon the Israelites and their enemies, it seems like the God of the Old Testament is primarily a God of judgment and vengeance. Yet when we read the New Testament accounts of the birth of Christ, His earthly ministry and miracles, and His vicarious death on the cross for the forgiveness of our sins, it's very obvious that the God of the New Testament is a God of love and grace.

So is the God of the Old Testament different from the God of the New Testament? And specifically, is the God of the Old Testament less gracious and loving than the God of the New Testament? Before answering these questions, let's consider these Old Testament facts:

- The God of the Old Testament parted the Red Sea and delivered the Israelites from Egyptian bondage, knowing that within three days the children of Israel would begin a repetitive cycle of grumbling against the very One who delivered them.

- The God of the Old Testament entered into a covenant with these same flawed, imperfect people knowing full well they would not keep it.

- The God of the Old Testament provided Moses with a plan for His people's redemption and forgiveness even as those very same people were building and worshipping a golden calf.

- Finally and climactically, the God of the Old Testament sent the glory of His magnificent, holy presence to inhabit a tent that was erected—by His own divine design—right in the very center of these same, sinful people.

The Old Testament record consistently confirms this fact: the God of the Old Testament is no different from the God of the New Testament. Throughout the Old Testament and in all of His dealings with His people Israel, God has continually proven Himself most gracious and loving.

History also consistently confirms another fact concerning the entire human race: "for all have sinned and fall short of the glory of God" (Romans 3:23, *NASB)*. Proof of this fact is painfully obvious to all of us. Sin wasn't just a problem for the Israelites. We freely admit that we are all sinners.

But please consider yet another mind-boggling fact that pre-dates both the Old Testament and the history of man: before God created man from the dust of the earth, before man willfully chose to sin, God had already provided the remedy for sin. The Bible says that Jesus, the Son of God, was "slain from the foundation of the world" (Revelations 13:8 *KJV*) —astounding proof and rock-solid evidence of the eternal love and grace of God.

No, God has not changed, but do you know what? God *can* change us: "Therefore, if anyone is in Christ, he is a new creation; the old has gone, the new has come" (2 Corinthians 5:17)—indisputable proof and irrefutable evidence of the love and grace of the unchanging God of the Old *and* New Testaments.

THIS WEEK'S
KEY PRINCIPLE:

*We glorify
God in our
everyday lives
by following
the pattern
of the
tabernacle.*

Day One

1. I hope today's Psalm is a comfort to you—it is to me. Though it may seem at times that the circumstances and events in our lives (and in our world) are spinning wildly out of control, we have this assurance: Our God is sovereign and omniscient. He is completely in control, and He is absolutely aware of everything that concerns His children. Whatever burden you are bearing, whatever struggle you are facing, meditate on today's Psalm. Then spend a few moments in prayer and praise before you begin this week's study.

> *The Lord is in His holy temple;*
> *the Lord is on His heavenly throne.*
> *He observes the sons of men; His eyes examine them.*
> Psalm 11:4

In last week's lesson, you saw the painstaking dedication of the Israelites as they undertook the construction of the tabernacle. God gave them the richly detailed blueprint for this structure, and they obeyed His design down to the smallest detail. As a result, when the construction was complete, the Israelites witnessed a miraculous and climactic event that would forever set them apart from all of the idol-worshipping nations that surrounded them: the literal, visible glory of God's presence filled the tabernacle and dwelt among them. Wow!

Today we'll be studying some of the details that preceded God's glorious infilling of the tabernacle. Within these details lies a wealth of symbolism that continues to speak to us today. As we discover and apply the symbolic truths contained in the tabernacle, may our lives also display the glory of God's presence (just as the tabernacle did) and set us apart as "a chosen race...a holy nation, a people for God's own possession" (1 Peter 2:9 *NASB).*

2. As you begin your study, briefly review the purpose of the tabernacle by reading Exodus 25:8. Underline the primary purpose of the tabernacle.

> *And let them construct a sanctuary for Me, that I may dwell among them.*
> —Exodus 25:8 *NASB*

3. In Exodus 25:10, right after God states His desire to dwell among the Israelites, God begins giving Moses the specific instructions for building His sanctuary, the tabernacle. Please review Exodus 25:10–22, then answer the following questions:

    a. According to verses 10 and 17, what are the first two things God commands Moses and the Israelites to construct?

    1) _____

    2) _____

b. According to verse 22, why were these two pieces of furniture so significant?

c. What do you think is symbolized by the fact that God's very first instructions regarding the construction of the tabernacle concerned these two specific pieces of furniture?

4. Let's look at a few other "firsts" found in Exodus as Moses and his people begin to construct the tabernacle. Please read the scriptures listed below, and record your answers to the following "firsts":

   a. Exodus 37:1–9—First furniture constructed: _____

   b. Exodus 40:1–2, 17—Date tabernacle was first erected: _____

   c. Exodus 40:3, 20–21a—First furniture placed inside the tabernacle: _____

5. In your opinion, what is the symbolism and significance of these "firsts"?

6. In Exodus 40:17–33, we see a long list of Moses' activities as he obediently set up the tabernacle according to God's exact instructions. Right before God's glory filled the tabernacle, Moses completed three final tasks. Please read the following scriptures and record these tasks:

   a. Exodus 40:29—Task: _____

   b. Exodus 40:30–32—Task: _____

   c. Exodus 40:33—Task: _____

7. Exodus 40:31 reveals that Moses, Aaron and his sons were the only ones allowed within the courtyard area of the tabernacle as the tasks (from Question 6) were completed and as God's glory filled the tabernacle. As you consider all of this, please answer the following questions:

a.   Why do you think God required Moses to offer the sacrifice *before* Moses, Aaron and his sons washed themselves? In other words, what does the order of these tasks symbolize?

b.   The Israelites had probably watched as Moses set up the tabernacle, offered the sacrifices, and washed with the priests at the laver. But as Moses completed his tasks that day by erecting curtains all around the outer court of the tabernacle area, the people's view would have been cut off from that point. What do you think that final task and those curtains symbolized as Moses prepared for God's presence to descend upon the tabernacle?

c.   Do you think that God's presence would have filled the tabernacle if Moses had followed God's instructions that day *but* had completed these activities in a different order? Please explain your answer.

Two other very interesting aspects about the tabernacle have great application for us today. First, the tabernacle was designed by God to be a portable, movable structure. All throughout the Israelites' journey to Canaan, the tabernacle moved with them from place to place. This aspect of the tabernacle taught them about their need for God's continual presence and about the reality of God's omnipresence. It also foreshadowed our need for God to dwell within us and to journey with us through our daily pilgrimage here on earth.

The second aspect of the tabernacle is that it was a temporal structure. Eventually the tabernacle was replaced by Solomon's temple (which was also temporary). The tabernacle was never intended to be a permanent structure. This temporal aspect would teach the Israelites that "the Most High does not live in houses made by men" (Acts 7:48), and it would foreshadow a time when God's presence would inhabit temporal, human "tents" as well.

8. Now please read Exodus 40:36–38, and answer the following questions:

   a. Who led the Israelites in all of their journeys? Please circle one.

   Moses   God   Aaron and the priests

   b. How did the Israelites know when and where to go, and when and where to stop?

9. As New Covenant believers, what "cloud" has God provided for us to follow? How can we see where God is leading us? Please read the following scriptures, then briefly describe the "clouds" God has given us to guide us in our earthly journey:

   a. John 13:15, 1 Peter 2:21

   b. John 16:13

   c. Psalm 119:105, 2 Peter 1:19–21

   d. James 1:5

   e. Proverbs 3:5–6

10. In what specific areas of your life do you need God's leadership? What has He revealed to you today about following His lead? Please journal your answers to these questions.

Insights

_____

_____

_____

_____

_____

Day Two

1. Today as you continue to study the tabernacle, make Psalm 27:4 your prayer. Ask God to use His Word to reveal His beauty to you in a life-changing way.

   One thing I ask of the Lord, this is what I seek:
   that I may dwell in the house of the Lord all the days of my life,
   to gaze upon the beauty of the Lord and to seek Him in His temple.
   Psalm 27:4

2 Begin your study by reading the following verses (noting the words "copy," "shadow," and "pattern"); then complete the work that follows:

   *If He (Christ) were on earth, He would not be a priest, for there are already men who offer the gifts prescribed by the law. They serve at a sanctuary that is a **copy** and **shadow** of what is in heaven. This is why Moses was warned when he was about to build the tabernacle: "See to it that you make everything according to the **pattern** shown you on the mountain."*

   —Hebrews 8:4–5

   a. Using the verses from Hebrews, please fill in the following blanks:
   Hebrews 8:4–5 The _____ is a copy/shadow of
   _____.

   b. Use a dictionary to complete the following sentences and define the words "copy," "shadow," and "pattern":

   A **copy** is _____

   _____

   A **shadow** is _____

   _____

   A **pattern** is _____

   _____

   c. Using the definitions above, briefly explain the primary truth taught in Hebrews 8:4–5.

The tabernacle is an Old Testament *type* which means it is a "representation or symbol of something to come."[1] In other words, it was a copy and a shadow—just as you've already seen—of a future reality. But what was it a copy and shadow of?

First, the tabernacle symbolizes the church. In Ephesians 2:19–22, the church is also described as a "holy temple," and as "a dwelling in which God lives by His Spirit." Secondly, since 1 Corinthians 6:19 (our key verse for this study) says that our "body is the temple of the Holy Spirit," the tabernacle also symbolizes the individual believer. Thirdly, the tabernacle represents and symbolizes heaven just as the verses you previously studied from Hebrews said. But most importantly, the tabernacle represents and symbolizes Christ (John 1:14, Hebrews 9–10). All throughout the details of the tabernacle, the future work and person of Christ are evident.

As a child, I attended Sunday school where I heard many stories about the tabernacle. I remember my Sunday school teachers would use a flannel board to illustrate and teach the basic truths of the Old Testament tabernacle. But it wasn't until I became an adult that I gained a true appreciation for the truths and symbolism of the tabernacle. In my late twenties, as a novice student of God's Word, I studied the tabernacle, and it was as if the Bible came alive with new meaning to me. That study, all those years ago, literally revolutionized my spiritual life as it gave me:

- a broader knowledge of God and His ways,
- a deeper appreciation for His love and grace,
- a greater understanding about how I could glorify God in my daily life,
- a new confidence and freedom in drawing near to His presence, and
- a joy and a delight in my Savior unlike any I had ever previously known.

Because that study of the tabernacle was so beneficial for me, I cannot help but think it will bless and benefit you as well. So for the rest of this week's study, we will be focusing on the tabernacle. Our study will be limited to its simple layout and sparse furnishings. Yet even within this very small scope, we will discover limitless treasures of symbolism and application for our lives—and make no mistake, *application* of scripture is our ultimate goal. As we begin our study of the tabernacle, this is my prayer: *Lord, teach us how to live daily in Your presence so that we may glo* **with** *Your glory* **for** *Your glory.*

3. The following picture is a diagram of the basic layout and furnishings of the tabernacle. Your assignment is to label this diagram by filling in the shaded blanks with the correct name of the furniture or area it describes. The furnishings and specific areas of the tabernacle are listed for you just below the diagram. The scriptures on this list will give you the location of each piece of furniture or specific area. Please read the scripture for each specific item, then label the tabernacle diagram by filling in the shaded blanks with the correct item or term. **NOTE: If you've studied the tabernacle before and you are already familiar with its layout, you may go ahead and label the diagram without looking up the scriptures.**

The Temple

The Tabernacle

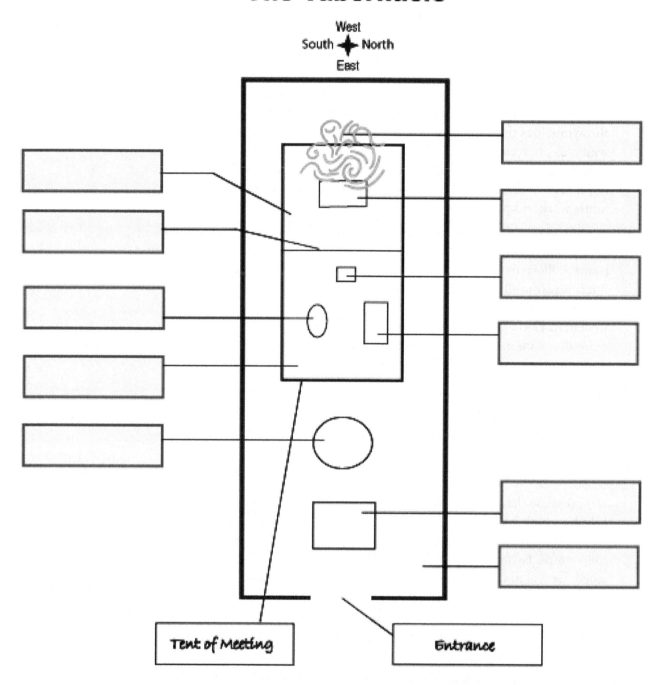

West

South ← → North

East

Tent of Meeting

Entrance

1. Ark / Mercy Seat or Atonement Cover - Exodus 25:21-22, 26:34
2. Brazen Altar - Exodus 40:6, 29
3. Table of Showbread - Exodus 26:35, 40:22-23
4. Brazen Laver/Basin - Exodus 40:7, 30
5. Lampstand - Exodus 26:35, 40:24
6. Veil - Exodus 26:31-33, 40:1
7. Altar of Incense - Exodus 40:5a, 26-27
8. Outer Courtyard - Exodus 40:8, 33
9. Holy Place - Exodus 26:33, Hebrews 9:2
10: Holy of Holies - Exodus 26:33, Hebrews 9:3
11. Presence & Glory of God - Exodus 40:34-35, 38

4. Now let's begin learning more about the ark and its covering and the mercy seat/atonement cover. Complete the following charts by:
    *   Reading the scriptures listed by most of the questions.
    *   Using any Bible commentaries you may have.
    *   Using Bible commentary sources online (examples: www.bibleclassics.com, www.biblegateway.com, and www.studylight.org).

    NOTE: Most of the commentaries included on the sites listed above were written by scholars who are theologically conservative and biblically sound.

The Ark:

What two materials were used to construct the ark? *Exodus 25:10–13*
How would these materials symbolize Christ?
Where was the ark located within the tabernacle, and what do you think this symbolized? *Exodus 25:21–22, 26:34*
What happened when Moses went near the ark? *Numbers 7:89*
Where was the ark located when the Israelites traveled, and why is this significant? *Numbers 10:11, 33–36*
Why was the ark always so significant to the Israelites? *1 Samuel 4:16–17, 21–22*

The Mercy Seat/Atonement Cover:

What single material was used to construct the mercy seat? *Exodus 25:17*

How would this material have symbolized Christ?

Where was the mercy seat located within the tabernacle, and what do you think its location symbolized? *Exodus 25:21–22, 26:34*

Who was allowed access to the mercy seat and how often? *Hebrews 9:6–7*

What event happened at the mercy seat, and what was its purpose? *Leviticus 16:3, 14–15, 32–34*

How did Christ fulfill the ministry of the mercy seat and abolish the need for atonement by an earthly priest? *Hebrews 9:11–14, 24, 10:14*

5. As you think about all you've studied today, what impact has it had upon your life? What is your response to what you've learned today?

_____

_____

_____

_____

_____

_____

_____

_____

_____

— ❧ *Day Three* ❧ —

1. Today's Psalm recounts God's deliverance of the Israelites and His faithfulness to them throughout their journey to the Promised Land. After you've read this Psalm, spend a few moments in prayer thanking God for His faithful guidance and leadership in your own life. Confess to Him your need for His leadership, and commit to follow wherever He may lead you today.

He guided them with the cloud by day and with light from the fire all night. Psalm 78:14

   As you began to see in yesterday's homework, the layout and furnishings of the tabernacle foreshadowed the church, the individual believer, heaven, and the person and work of Christ. From the majestic ark of the covenant to the humble tent pegs, from the colors of the priests' clothing to the acacia wood, gold, and bronze used to construct its furnishings, every selection and choice God made concerning the tabernacle is symbolic.

   My sister, as you continue studying the tabernacle, this is the desire of my heart for you: I want you to become so thoroughly familiar with the layout, furnishings, and symbolism of the tabernacle that you will be able to spiritually "walk through it" on a daily basis from this point forward. Why? *Because the pattern presented through the tabernacle system of worship will enable you to glorify God every day of your life.* And remember (just in case you've forgotten in the midst of studying all of these tabernacle details), that's exactly what this study is all about!

2. Although I realize you may not yet see the practical application of the tabernacle, by the final day of this week's study you definitely will. But for now, please review the diagram of the tabernacle that you labeled in yesterday's study. Do your very best to memorize its layout and its furnishings. Trust me, you'll be glad you did!

The Temple

3. Continue learning more about the tabernacle by completing the following charts just as you did in yesterday's homework. Please read the scriptures listed, and feel free to use your Bible commentaries and/or online study tools.

Altar of Incense

What two materials were used to construct the altar of incense? *Exodus 30:1–5*
How would these materials have symbolized Christ?
Where was this altar located within the tabernacle, and what would its location have symbolized? *Exodus 30:6*
What was the purpose of this altar? *Exodus 30:7–10*
How often was it used for the purposes stated above? *Exodus 30:7–8*
How does this altar symbolize Christ? *John 17:1–26, Hebrews 7:25*

Table of Showbread

What two materials were used to construct the table? *Exodus 25:23–30*

How would these materials have symbolized Christ?

What were the items that were placed upon the table called? *Exodus 25:30, Leviticus 24:5–6*

How often and when was this table set? *Leviticus 24:8*

What happened to the bread on this table? *Leviticus 24:9*

How does the bread symbolize Christ and our relationship with Him? *John 6:32–35, Mark 14:22*

Lampstand

What single material was used to construct the lampstand? *Exodus 25:31–40*

How would this material symbolize Christ?

What was the purpose of the lampstand, and what would it have enabled the priests to do? *Exodus 25:37*

What was the source of the light, and what does that product symbolize? *Exodus 27:20*

How often did the lampstand burn, and how was it cared for? *Exodus 27:20–21, 30:7, Leviticus 24:1–4*

How does the lampstand symbolize Christ? Luke 2:32 (be sure to check the context), *John 8:12, 1 Corinthians 4:5, Revelation 21:23*

4. Your focus today has been on the Old Testament tabernacle, but I want to bring you back to the primary focus of this entire study by reviewing the key verses for this study, 1 Corinthians 6:19–20. I hope you've memorized these verses by now. Test your memory by filling in the following blanks:

Or do you not _____ that your body is a _____ ____ ____ _____ _____ who is in you, whom you have from God, and that _____ _____ _____ _____ _____? For you have been _____ _____ ____ _____: therefore _____ _____ _____ _____ _____.

—1 Corinthians 6:19–20 *NASB*

5. How has your study of the tabernacle encouraged you to glorify God through your life, and what insights has the Holy Spirit given you today?

_____

_____

_____

_____

_____

_____

_____

_____

_____

Insights

— ❧ *Day Four* ❧ —

1. Please follow the instructions given in today's Psalm before you begin your time of study in God's exalted Word.

I will bow down toward Your holy temple
and will praise Your name for Your love and Your faithfulness,
for You have exalted above all things Your name and Your word.
Psalm 138:2

Pray Today

2. Conclude your study of the furnishings of the tabernacle by completing the following charts just as you've previously done. Remember to read the scriptures that are listed, but also feel free to use your Bible commentaries and/or online study tools.

The Temple

83

Laver/Basin

What was the purpose of the laver? *Exodus 30:17–21*
How does the laver symbolize Christ? *Ephesians 5:25–27, I John 1:7*
How often did the priests use the laver? *Exodus 30:19–21*
Where was the laver located, and what would its location have symbolized? *Exodus 40:7*

Altar

What materials were used to construct the altar? *Exodus 27:1–8*
How would these materials symbolize Christ?
Where was the altar located, and what would its location have symbolized? *Exodus 40:6, 29*
What was the purpose of the altar? *Exodus 29:18, 40:29*
For whom would the priests offer sacrifices? *Hebrews 5:3*
How often was the altar used, and what did this reveal? *Hebrews 10:1, 3, 11*
How does the altar symbolize Christ? *Ephesians 5:2, Hebrews 10:10–12*

3. I trust your study of the tabernacle has revealed God's love for you in a beautiful, new way. I also hope it has given you a deeper appreciation for Christ's work on your behalf. If it has, pour out your heart on paper and express your gratitude to Him.

_____

_____

_____

_____

_____

_____

_____

Day Five

1. Rejoice in the truth of today's Psalm by praising Him for the light He has given you this week. Ask Him to continue to shed light upon His Word as you begin another day of study.

The Lord is God,
and He has made His light shine upon us.
Psalm 118:27

Just as God chose to inhabit and reveal His glory through the beautifully designed yet humble tent of the tabernacle, God has also chosen to inhabit and reveal His glory through the beautifully designed (Psalm 139) yet humble tents of our bodies. The tabernacle magnificently foreshadows the life of the believer. Today we will "walk" through the tabernacle in a deeply personal way and learn how it teaches us to glorify God.

2. You will begin your "walk" at the entrance to the tabernacle. As you've probably already noticed (from the diagram of the tabernacle that you completed earlier this week), there is only one entrance into the tabernacle. What does this mean to you today? Please read the following scriptures, and note how you can enter into God's presence:

a. John 10:7–9

b. John 14:6

3. If you have entered through the Door, you'll now proceed a few more steps to the altar. It is the place of sacrifice. What does God require of you here? How can you glorify Him at this altar? To answer these questions, please read the following scriptures, and record what you learn:

   a. Romans 6:11–13

   b. Romans 12:1

4. All throughout the book of Leviticus there is a repeated phrase regarding the sacrifices that were offered at the altar. The phrase is "an offering to the Lord…pleasing to the Lord." But this phrase, of course, refers to the sacrifices made under the Old Covenant system.

   Are there any "sacrifices" you, a New Covenant believer, can make that will be "pleasing to the Lord"? What offerings can you bring to Him today? To answer these questions, please read the following scriptures and record what you learn:

   a. Psalm 19:14

   b. Mark 12:33

   c. Philippians 4:18 (please read verses 14–17 to understand the context)

   d. Hebrews 13:15–16

5. As you continue your walk through the tabernacle, you will come to the laver. It is the place of cleansing. What will purify and cleanse you? How can you be sanctified and set apart as holy? Please read the following scriptures and record your answers to these questions:

    a.   John 17:17

    b.   Titus 3:5

    c.   1 John 1:9

6. You are now prepared to enter into the holy place inside the tent of meeting. The holy place is the place of ministry and worship. As you go inside, you will notice the glow and the brightness of the golden lampstand. It illuminates the room because it is fueled by pure oil, which represents the Holy Spirit. How does the lampstand symbolize your life in Christ? What does it teach you about glorifying God? Please read the following scriptures, and then record your answers to these questions:

    a.   Matthew 5:14–16

    b.   John 15:26–27, 16:13–15

    c.   Philippians 2:15

    d.   1 John 1:6–7

7. Now look to your right, and you will see the golden table of showbread. It is the place of fellowship. For a beautiful example of this kind of fellowship, please read Acts 2:41–47, and record how God is glorified through the ministry of fellowship.

8. In the very center of the holy place is the altar of incense. As it continually burns, its fragrance fills the tent of meeting. How does it symbolize your life in Christ? What can it teach you about glorifying God? Please answer these questions by reading the following scriptures and recording your answers:

   a.   Revelation 5:8, 8:3

   b.   Ephesians 6:18

   c.   1 Thessalonians 5:17

   d.   James 5:13–16

9. You now stand before the most sacred place within the entire tabernacle: the holy of holies. Unlike the Old Testament priests, however, your admittance into the holy of holies is *uninhibited* and *unlimited*. You have direct access to God's presence. To understand how this has been made possible, please read these magnificent scriptures:

   And [on the cross] Jesus cried out again with a loud voice, and yielded up His spirit. And behold, the veil of the temple was torn in two from top to bottom...   —Matthew 27:50–51

   By one sacrifice (Christ) has made perfect forever those who are being made holy. The Holy Spirit also testifies to us about this. First He says: "This is the covenant I will make with them after that time, says the Lord. I will put My laws in their hearts, and I will write them on their minds." Then He adds "Their sins and lawless acts I will remember no more." And where these have been forgiven, there is no longer any sacrifice for sin.   —Hebrews 10:14–18

The Temple

How should you respond to all that your faithful High Priest, Jesus Christ, has done for you? I think the writer of Hebrews said it best:

> *Therefore, brothers, since we have confidence to enter the Most Holy Place by the blood of Jesus, by a new and living way opened for us through the curtain, that is, His body, and since we have a great Priest over the house of God, let us draw near to God with a sincere heart in full assurance of faith, having our hearts sprinkled to cleanse us from a guilty conscience and having our bodies washed with pure water.*

—Hebrews 10:19–22

10. And that is exactly what I want you to do right now. Drop to your knees. Lift up your hands. Respond to the life Christ has given you by confidently drawing near to Him with absolutely no doubt about His love for you. After all, He's the One who has freely and completely cleansed you with His blood, purifying you to become His *holy temple*. Hallelujah, what a Savior!

How I pray that your "walk" through the tabernacle was meaningful and transformational for you. Let this be the first of many, many "walks" you take throughout your lifetime as you seek to pattern your life according to the truths taught in the tabernacle.

In your daily prayer time, in your workplace, in your home, or in your car, take a spiritual "walk" through the tabernacle. Begin at the altar by offering yourself to God as a living sacrifice. Move to the laver and confess, repent, and be cleansed from your sin. Enter into the holy place by praying, interceding, serving, fellowshipping, and witnessing to others. Experience God's glory as you enjoy intimate communion with Him and the supernatural power of His presence. Choose daily to allow your life to become a place where God's glory dwells.

11. Close your time of study by reflecting upon what God has revealed to you. Journal your thoughts by completing the sentences below:

My Journal

This Week the Lord...

_____

_____

_____

_____

_____

_____

_____

_____

As a Result, I...

_____
_____
_____
_____
_____
_____
_____
_____
_____

❦

The other day, I was trying to imagine what it must have been like to see God's visible presence every day and every night as the Israelites did on their journey to Canaan. I envision them slipping outside their tents the very first thing in the morning just to feast their eyes upon the glory and majesty of God's presence hovering over the tabernacle. And each evening I imagine they'd want to take just one last look at the fiery pillar before retiring to their tents to sleep. The awesome glory of God's presence must have dazzled them day and night.

But just about the time I began to think, "Wow! I'd really like to see God's presence every day like that," my mind was suddenly gripped by this thought: God's presence lives within me right *now*. I woke up *this* morning, and His presence was with me. I'll go to bed in a few hours, and His presence will *still* be with me. It felt like an epiphany, a revival of my spiritual senses.

All of this thinking soon made me realize something about myself, something disturbing and unsettling, and—worst of all—something that is too often true: *I take God's presence for granted.* I walk around with Him all the time. I converse and commune with Him freely. I enjoy my daily time of Bible reading and prayer. But in some ways, God's presence has just become "the usual"—like when I go to my favorite Mexican restaurant and order the same old usual No. 6 Chicken Enchilada Plate without even taking time to look at the menu. Do not think for a minute that I enjoy admitting this to you. I share it only because maybe, just maybe, *you* are a lot like me.

After a little more thinking, I tend to believe the Israelites may have been very much like me (and maybe you, too). They probably got up and went outside some mornings to gather "the usual"—manna. Then they made breakfast and began going about their ordinary daily routine. That evening they had their quail dinner, cleaned up the dishes, and put the kids to bed. Then they tucked themselves in and nodded off to sleep, never even conscious of the fiery pillar of God's presence illuminating the night skies above them. I imagine that from time to time a woman might even whisper to her husband right before they both fell asleep, "Honey, you know, I didn't notice, but was the "cloud" out today?"

Each day in your homework, I ask you to record or journal the insights God is giving you as a result of your study. Allow me to put the shoe on the other foot for a few more lines and share with you what God is teaching me as I write this study. God is reawakening me to the *wonder of His presence*—in *me*. And you know what? His presence in me is *far* better than any cloud or fiery pillar!

I don't know what God is doing in your life, but if you need a reawakening of the wonder of His presence like I do, here's a powerful little truth that's sure been reigniting the fire in my heart these days: "Christ in you, the hope of glory" (Colossians 1:27 *NASB)*.

Sister, we have no excuses. Christ is *in us*. And you know what that means. Ready…set…***glo!***

The Temple: The Tabernacle— A Picture of Your Life in Christ

<u>Key Principle</u>: *We glorify God in our everyday lives*
by following the pattern of the tabernacle.

I. The Significance of the Tabernacle

A. It was the place of _____ _____ . *Ex. 25:8*

B. It symbolized a future time when God's _____ would _____
within us. *John 14:20*

II. The Tabernacle Reveals

A. God's _____ to _____ with His people.

B. Our _____ for a _____ with God.

C. God _____ _____ to us through _____/Christ.

D. Our way to _____ a relationship with God by _____ in Christ.

III. The Symbolism

A. The Tabernacle Symbolizes:

1. The _____ and _____ of Christ. *John 1:14*

2. The _____. *Eph. 2:19–21*

3. The _____ _____. *1 Cor. 6:19*

B. The Three Primary Areas of the Tabernacle Symbolize:

1. The Outer Court = The place of _____ and _____.

2. The Inner Court/Holy Place = The place of _____, _____ and

_____.

3. The Holy of Holies = The place of _____ _____; our

most personal _____ with God.

IV. How It Applies to Us Today

Reveals Christ—Who Has Met My Every Need

1. I need a _____ to God.

   The Single Entrance

   Christ is the _____. *John 10:9, 14:6*

2. I need a _____ for my _____.

   The Brazen Altar

   Christ is the _____. *John 1:29*

3. I need _____.

   The Brazen Laver

   Christ has _____ me. *Titus 3:5*

4. I need _____ for my daily _____.

   The Golden Lampstand

   Christ is the _____ of my _____.
   John 1:4

5. I need someone to _____ for me.

   The Altar of Incense

   Christ is my _____. *Heb. 7:25*

6. I need spiritual _____ and _____.

   The Table of Showbread

   Christ is my bread and my _____.
   Rev. 3:20

7. I need _____ with God.

   The Ark/Mercy Seat

   Christ's _____ is my access.
   Heb. 10:19–22

Gives Me a "Spiritual Checklist"

To glorify God in my everyday life, I must:

❏ Go to the _____ daily. *Rom. 12:1*

❏ Go to the laver of _____ _____
   and allow Him to wash and _____
   me daily. *John 17:17, James 1:23–25*

❏ Let His _____ within me shine
   as a _____ to others. *Mt. 5:16*

❏ Spend time in _____ to God
   and in _____ for
   others. *1 Thess. 5:17*

❏ Participate in _____
   and in _____ with other
   believers. *Heb. 10:24–25, 1 Peter 4:10*

Results:

_____ with God.

_____ before God. *Heb. 4:16*

You'll be _____ _____.

You'll _____ _____.

The Temple: MATTERS OF THE HEART

Change. Now that's a word that always makes me feel just a little bit uneasy. I much prefer predictable, comfortable, and secure. But just about the time I begin to feel all settled and at ease, change arrives to ruffle my nice, unruffled routine.

There's an old saying: The only thing constant is change. It's only a saying and it's certainly not a scripture, but it sounds to me as if it could have come straight out of the book of Proverbs. Change. It's the one sure thing we can always count on—whether we like it or not.

True, sometimes we deliberately choose change; for instance, when we choose to go off to college, or we choose to get married. We may choose to begin a new career; or we may even choose to have a child or two, or three, or four, or more. But these are not the kinds of changes that seem to upset us, because these changes are ones we have planned, prayed about, and have carefully considered— well, OK, maybe not every single one of those children.

The kind of change that unsettles us most is the unanticipated, unexpected, and unforeseen kind of change—the kind we would *never* choose. Like the routine doctor's appointment that reveals a startling diagnosis. Or the sudden upheaval of a move that uproots us from family, friends, and everything that is familiar. It may be the abrupt layoff from the job in which we had plans to retire; or even the phone call from the school that signals our child is struggling and can't keep up with the rest of the class. These are the kinds of changes we do not choose—yet they arrive nonetheless.

After 46 years of living life, I think I'm finally beginning to get it when it comes to change, and this is what I've concluded: Since change always *has* been and always *will* be a constant part of life, that surely must mean that God loves change. Brilliant, huh? But do you know why I believe God loves change so much? Two reasons: (1) because change is a chisel He can use to change us, and (2) because changed lives glorify Him.

Think about it. Without change, our hearts would very likely become calloused and cool, prideful and self-sufficient. Without change, we'd probably be spiritually stunted, carnal, and immature. But *change*. It brings us to our knees, it drives us to His Word, and it compels us to depend desperately upon our Father. When we choose to respond to change like that, our hearts become tender, our love for God grows, and our very lives are transformed—changed—giving evidence of God's power and glory. Yes, I believe God loves change.

Change will be one of the themes of this week's lesson. For forty years Moses led the sons of Israel through the wilderness. For forty years they camped with God. And for forty years God's visible glory dwelt within their very midst— but change was on its way. Moses would die. A new leader would take over. After they entered Canaan, the twelve tribes of Israel would no longer remain together but would, instead, be separated and distributed throughout the land.

THIS WEEK'S
KEY PRINCIPLE:

We glorify God in our everyday lives by following Him obediently and by giving Him priority.

But far greater changes than these would await the Israelites in their new land. The pillar of fire and the cloud of God's presence would no longer be visible to them. The tabernacle would be set up in the city of Gilgal, and the Israelites would no longer experience the daily, constant influence of its presence within their midst. Change. Lots and lots of change.

Change always leads to choices, and choices are ultimately always made within the heart—which is the primary target for God's chisel of change. You see, although the changes we experience may be outward—an unexpected move, a child who is struggling, the loss of a job, etc.—God's target is always inward. It's the heart that God really wants to change, because only those whose hearts have been changed can truly glorify Him.

Change: it is essential for salvation.

> *And (Jesus) said: "I tell you the truth, unless you **change** and become like little children, you will never enter the kingdom of heaven."*
> —Matthew 18:3

Change: it is a present-tense command to every believer.

> *Do not conform any longer to the pattern of this world, but be [**changed**] by the renewing of your mind.*
> —Romans 12:2

Change: it is a future certainty for every Christian.

> *Listen, I tell you a mystery: We will not all sleep, but we will all be **changed**—in a flash, in the twinkling of an eye, at the last trumpet. For the trumpet will sound, the dead will be raised imperishable, and we will be **changed**.*
> —1 Corinthians 15:51–52

God loves change. God uses change to change us. Change glorifies God. Finally at age 46, I get it. The challenge, however, is: will I say it, and dare I pray it? Yes, I choose to say, "Lord, let the change begin. Change me." What about you—will you say that, too?

— ✦ *Day One* ✦ —

1. How I thank God that He can give us a new heart, and that He is able to continually renew and purify that heart! As you begin your week of study, ask God to do a brand new work of purification and renewal within your heart that will be evident throughout your life today.

Create in me a pure heart, O God,
and renew a steadfast spirit within me. Psalm 51:10

Over the past few weeks, we have been tracing the way God revealed Himself and His glory to Moses and the Israelites. We've looked back in time to see how God taught His people to worship and glorify Him through the sacrificial system of the Old Covenant tabernacle.

For forty years Moses and the Israelites worshipped God at the tabernacle as they journeyed with Him to the Promised Land of Canaan. The glory of God's presence continually appeared above the tent of meeting in the form of a cloud by day and a pillar of fire by night. Yet even though the people witnessed God's visible presence, even though they made their sacrificial offerings, and even though they observed the laws and statutes of the Old Covenant, had their *hearts* been changed?

Just before the Israelites entered Canaan, Moses spoke to his people one final time. Today we will study that message. From Moses' words, we will learn the truth about the hearts of God's people. We will also learn a very important truth we must all apply as we seek to glorify God: Only those whose hearts have been changed can truly glorify God.

My dear sister, today as you study His Word, allow God to examine your heart.

2. In Deuteronomy 9, Moses explains why God will give the Israelites the land of Canaan. Please read Deuteronomy 9:1–7, and answer the following questions:

   a.   Why did God give the Israelites the land of Canaan?

   b.   Did the Israelites earn the land of Canaan as a reward because of their own righteousness? Please circle one: Yes   No

   c.   According to verse 7, what is the spiritual condition of the heart of the people even as they are about to enter the Promised Land?

   d.   Do you think the Israelites believed their hearts were righteous? Please circle one: Yes   No

   e.   Had the hearts of the Israelites changed during their forty-year pilgrimage with God? Please circle one: Yes   No

f. After journeying with God for forty years, after all they had witnessed God do for them, the condition of their hearts seems almost impossible to fathom. What application does this knowledge have for us today?

3. Genesis 12:1–7 is a record of God's covenant with Abraham. Please read this passage, and answer the following questions:

a. What did God tell Abraham to do (v. 1)?

b. What did God promise He would do for Abraham (vv. 2–3)?

c. How did Abraham respond (vv. 4–6)?

d. What was God's promise to Abraham when he arrived in the land (v. 7)?

e. As you look back at Question 2a and b, how does God's promise to Abraham relate to the people of Moses' day?

4. What were God's requirements of the people when they entered the land of Canaan? To answer this question, please read the following scriptures and record your answers:

    a.   Deuteronomy 6:1–7 (Note especially how they were commanded to love God.)

    b.   Deuteronomy 10:12–13

5. Please read Deuteronomy 10:15–22, and answer the following questions:

    a.   According to verse 15, what did God do?

    b.   What, then, does God require them to do (v. 16)?

    c.   As you think about their spiritual condition (noted earlier in Question 2c from Deuteronomy 9:7), what do you think God means when He figuratively tells them to "Circumcise their heart" in Deuteronomy 10:16.

    d.   If God asked them to do this, do you think, then, that it was possible for them to do it? Please circle one: Yes   No

    e.   From what you have previously studied about Moses, do you think his heart was circumcised? Please circle one, and explain your answer: Yes   No

6. Deuteronomy 28 clearly states the basic conditions and promises of the Old Covenant. Please quickly scan this chapter (especially noting verses 1–2 and verse 15). Then briefly summarize the promises of the Old Covenant by completing the following sentences:

   a. If they obeyed the Lord and His commands, they would receive

   _____.

   b. If they disobeyed the Lord and His commands, they would receive

   _____.

7. Please read Deuteronomy 28:47–52, 63–65 carefully. Then place a check in each box that correctly describes the results of Israel's disobedience.

   ☐ They would be taken captive to serve their enemies.

   ☐ They would suffer hunger, thirst, and physical deprivation.

   ☐ Another nation would plunder their resources.

   ☐ They would be torn from the land and scattered.

   NOTE: Other repercussions for Israel's disobedience are included in this chapter, but some are simply too awful to include.

8. Please read Deuteronomy 30:1–2, 15–20, and answer the following questions:

   a. Will the Israelites keep the covenant? Please circle one: Yes   No

   b. How could they have chosen blessing instead of cursing (vv. 16 and 20)?

9. Is there any hope for Israel? Please read Deuteronomy 30:5–6, and record what God will do for them one day.

10. What has God taught you today about the heart and about His own heart?

11. Has there been a time in your life when you turned away from your own stubbornness and rebellion and allowed God to circumcise your heart? If so, please briefly describe how and when that change of heart occurred. If you are unsure whether your heart has ever been changed, please turn to the back of this workbook and read the page entitled *A Change of Heart*. God can give *you* a brand new heart today!

12. Is there any stubbornness or rebellion in your heart today? Are you wrestling with God about an issue in your life? If so, will you write out a prayer to the Lord and surrender that issue to Him right now? Blessing awaits you, dear sister.

_____

_____

_____

_____

_____

_____

_____

_____

_____

Day Two

1. Today's Psalm is the expression of one who diligently and purposefully sought to keep his heart pure. No, David was not perfect, but he was described as "a man after (God's) own heart" (1 Samuel 13:14). Become a woman after God's heart, and allow David's psalm to lead you into a time of prayer. Ask God to uncover any sin and wrong attitudes within your heart. Then quietly listen for His answer. Confess any sin before Him, and commit to making things right with others whom you may have sinned against. Continue in prayer until God has thoroughly examined your heart and until you know you can pass the "test," just as David said he could.

> *Though You probe my heart and examine me at night,*
> *though You test me, You will find nothing;*
> *I have resolved that my mouth will not sin.* Psalm 17:3

For the rest of this week, we will be fast-forwarding through the history of Israel prior to the birth of Christ. *Our primary goal will be to learn from Israel's example—the good and the bad—how to have a heart that glorifies God.* We'll also be learning how the tabernacle became the *temple*. So, hang on. We'll be moving at warp speed for the next several days!

2. Today you will be doing a study in contrasts. First you will study Joshua, whom God appointed as Moses' successor. Please complete the following chart by reading the scriptures listed. Then record your answer to each question:

Joshua

What did God command Joshua to do? *Joshua 1:2*
What was God's promise to Joshua? *Joshua 1:3–5, 9*
What was God's repeated exhortation to Joshua? *Joshua 1:6–7, 9*
How did Joshua respond to God's commands and exhortation? *Joshua 1:10–11, 3:1*
What instructions and promise did Joshua give to the people before they crossed the Jordan River, and what do they reveal about Joshua? *Joshua 3:5* **NOTE: The cloud and the fiery pillar representing God's presence were no longer with the Israelites. Also, at this particular time of the year, the Jordan River was very deep, very strong, and very swift.**
Briefly describe God's instructions to Joshua about crossing the Jordan and what happened to the priests and the people as they crossed the Jordan. *Joshua 3:7–17*

What did this miraculous event reveal to the people about God? *Joshua 3:10*

Many years later, after the Israelites had taken possession of the land and Joshua was about to die, Joshua spoke one final message to his people. What does Joshua exhort the people to do, and how do the people respond? *Joshua 24:14–18*

What did Joshua know about the people, and what does this reveal about their hearts? *Joshua 24:14b, 19, 23*

What does Joshua reveal about his own heart? *Joshua 24:15*

3. For the next 300 years, the nation of Israel was ruled by a series of judges. This period of Israel's history is best described in Judges 2:7–17. Please read this passage. Then briefly summarize the Israelites' relationship with God after Joshua and his generation died.

4. Our study in contrasts continues as you observe a priest named Eli and his two sons Hophni and Phinehas. Eli and his sons served as priests at the conclusion of the historical era of the judges. As priests, they were considered leaders in Israel. Please complete the following chart by reading the scriptures listed. Then record your answer to each question:

Eli and Sons

What did you learn about Eli's sons? *1 Samuel 2:12–17, 22* **NOTE: These scriptures also reveal the tabernacle was now in Shiloh.**

How did Eli respond to his sons' behavior, and what was the result? *1 Samuel 2:22–25*

What did the man of God say Eli had done especially with regard to his sons, and what does this reveal about Eli's heart? *1 Samuel 2:27–29*

How would God deal with Eli and his sons? *1 Samuel 2:31–34*

What did the Israelite army, Hophni and Phinehas do with the ark of the covenant and why? What were they counting on? *1 Samuel 4:1–5*

What was the result of this tactic? *1 Samuel 4:6–18*

Why did this happen? What had God previously revealed to the man of God and to Samuel? *1 Samuel 2:30–32, 3:11–14*

What did the ark's capture symbolize? *1 Samuel 4:19–22*

5. What enabled Joshua to glorify God with his life?

6. What prevented Eli and his sons from glorifying God with their lives?

7. How is the Lord exhorting you to be strong and courageous in your life, and how will you respond?

_____

_____

_____

_____

_____

_____

_____

_____

⟡ *Day Three* ⟡

1. Let today's Psalm express the cry of your heart. Spend a few minutes prayerfully seeking God's face before you begin your study.

   My heart says of You, "Seek His face!"
   Your face, Lord, I will seek. Psalm 27:8

   As you learned yesterday, the ark of the covenant was captured during Israel's battle with the Philistines. The ark had always symbolized the place of God's presence and glory. Today you'll study some very interesting history regarding the ark as we continue our fast-forward through Israel's past.

   Throughout the days of the judges, the hearts of God's people were far from Him. But a better day was about to dawn. David would become their king, and one of his first tasks would be to restore God's glory to Israel. Even though his heart was passionately committed to the Lord, David still had a lot to learn about God. And guess what? He'll learn it the *hard* way—just like *we* usually do!

2. What happened to the ark of the covenant after it was taken by the Philistines? Please take time to read 1 Samuel 5–7:2; then summarize briefly what you learn about the ark by answering the following questions:

   a. What happened while the ark was in the house of Dagon, and what did it reveal about God (1 Samuel 5:1–6)?

   b. What did the Philistines do with the ark, and what was the result (1 Samuel 5:7–12)?

   c. What did the idolatrous priests and diviners in Philistine counsel the people to do, and what historical fact were they aware of that influenced their counsel (1 Samuel 6:1–9)?

   d. What happened to the ark, and how did the Israelites respond to the ark's return (1 Samuel 6:10–15)?

   e. Ultimately, what did the Israelites do, and what did they learn about God (1 Samuel 6:19–20)?

   f. What became of the ark of the covenant (1 Samuel 6:21–7:2)?

Several years later, Saul was appointed king over Israel. During his reign, the original tabernacle was set up at Nob, and later at Gibeon. Both of these cities were near Jerusalem. Priests ministered there, and sacrifices were offered. But the ark—the symbol of God's presence—remained in Eleazar's care at Kiriath-jearim. For this reason, and because the people were now dispersed throughout the land of Israel, the tabernacle itself had lost much of its significance. But remember, in its original design, the tabernacle was never meant to be a permanent structure. It was only a shadow and a symbol of things to come (Hebrews 9:8–11).

Saul's heart (and as you'll remember, the *heart* is the focus of this week's study) became proud and God rejected Him as Israel's king. God sought a man to lead Israel who had a heart for Him, and He found that man in David.

After Saul's death, David became king. It was a new beginning for Israel. Their hopes were high, and their hearts desired to embrace and experience God's leadership over them once more. Using a profound and devastating lesson that God knew His people needed to learn, God reminded them how to glorify Him. It's a lesson we need to be reminded of as well.

3. In this assignment, you will be reading parallel accounts from 2 Samuel and 1 Chronicles of an event that happened at the beginning of David's reign. Both of these books record this same event, but you will gain more details and a greater knowledge by reading both accounts.

Please read 2 Samuel 6:1–15, 1 Chronicles 13, and 1 Chronicles 15:1–28; *carefully observe the details they relate.* Also, please visualize these events in your mind as you read them. After you've read and meditated upon these passages, record your answers to the questions below. **NOTE: Uzzah was a Levite. For further insight, please read Exodus 25:14, Numbers 4:15, and Joshua 3:3, 14.**

a. What did God teach David and the Israelites about honoring and glorifying Him through this experience?

b. What do you think David may have learned about his own heart that day?

c.   What future effect do you think this would have had upon David as he led Israel?

d.   What principles can be learned from this account?

4.   What insight and application has the Holy Spirit given to you as you have meditated upon the account of David's experience with the ark?

_____

_____

_____

_____

_____

_____

_____

Day Four

1.   What are you doing with the truths God is teaching you? Oh, how I pray that you are walking in obedience to them. Sometimes it's easy to just rush in and do your Bible study, check it off your list, and then move on to whatever is next on your schedule. Today, before you begin your study, take this Psalm before the Lord in prayer, and commit to walking in the truths He is faithfully teaching you.

Teach me Your way, O Lord, and I will walk in Your truth;
give me an undivided heart, that I may fear Your name.
Psalm 86:11

David was king over all Israel and Judah for 33 years. Throughout his reign in Jerusalem, the ark of the covenant remained in a tent David had pitched for it. Although David wanted to build a house for God's presence, the Lord would not allow him to fulfill that desire.

Before he died, David appointed his son Solomon to become Israel's next king, and God appointed Solomon to a grand and magnificent task. God called Solomon to build a sanctuary for His presence. It would become the central focus for the entire nation of Israel. This structure, of course, was the temple.

Today you will study the glorious splendor of the dedication of Solomon's temple, but you will also learn about its inglorious destruction. And what you will discover is that the destruction of the temple was directly tied to matters of the *heart.*

2. Solomon began his reign so well. He did so many things right. Please read 2 Chronicles 1:1–13 to see a significant event that marked the beginning of Solomon's reign. Then answer the following questions:

   a. Where did Solomon go, and what did he do there (vv. 3–6)?

   b. What happened at this place later that night (vv. 7–13)?

   c. What does this reveal about Solomon's heart toward God?

3. Over the next several years, Solomon began and completed the greatest work of his entire life: building the temple in Jerusalem. Except for the ark, new furnishings were built and placed within the temple. 1 Kings 8 records the events of the day the temple was dedicated. Please read the following scriptures, and record your answers to each question:

   a. 1 Kings 8:1–4—What articles were brought up and placed in the temple?

b. 1 Kings 8:10–23—What happened when the ark was placed within the Holy of Holies?

c. 1 Kings 8:57–61—As Solomon concluded the dedication, what did he specifically ask God to do for the people, and what did he exhort the people to do regarding their hearts?

4. 2 Chronicles 7 records what happened at the conclusion of the temple dedication service, as well as God's words to Solomon soon after. Please read the following scriptures, and record your answers to each question:

a. 2 Chronicles 7:1–3—What happened after Solomon concluded his prayer?

b. 2 Chronicles 7:19–22—What were God's words of warning to Solomon regarding the Israelites and the temple?

5. Many years later, after a long period of peace, prosperity, and success as Israel's king, Solomon chose not to heed the warning God had given him. He had seen God's glory. He had seen fire fall from heaven consuming the sacrifice. He had heard God speak to him on several occasions and God appeared to him twice. And he had been blessed by God like no other man before him. Please read 1 Kings 11:1–10 and underline every mention of the word "heart." What happened to Solomon? How could he spurn God after all God had done for him?

6. According to 1 Kings 11:11–13, what was the result of Solomon's sin?

Solomon's sin was just the beginning of Israel's downfall. After Solomon died, the temple stood for over 300 years. However, the Israelites, the priests, and kings eventually spiraled downward into sin and idolatry. As a result, Israel experienced God's cursing. They were taken captive from their land by the Assyrians and the Babylonians, and the city of Jerusalem and the temple were destroyed. All of the beautiful furnishings—including the ark—and all of the treasures of the temple were plundered by Israel's enemies, just as God had promised.

Yet even while Israel was in captivity, God gave them hope for their future. Their hope—and ours—would be a New Covenant and with it, a new *heart*.

7. Please read the following scriptures, and record what you learn about the New Covenant and how it would differ from the Old Covenant:

   a.   Ezekiel 36:26–28

   b.   Ezekiel 37:26–28

8. Only you and the Lord know the answer to this question: Has God given you a new heart? Please circle one: Yes   No

9. If you answered "no" to Question 8, or if you are unsure, please read the article, *A Change of Heart* included in the final pages of this workbook.

10. If you answered "yes" to Question 8, then please answer this: is your heart fully and wholly devoted to God?   Yes   No

11. If you answered "no" to Question 8, please take a moment to read today's Psalm, printed at the beginning of this lesson. Now spend some time with the Lord in prayer. Confess your divided heart to Him, and ask Him to give you an undivided, fully devoted heart for Him.

Insights

12. What insight has the Holy Spirit given to you through your study today?

_____

_____

_____

_____

_____

_____

_____

— ✑ *Day Five* ✑ —

Pray Today

1. As you prepare to study God's Word, prayerfully set your heart on obeying Him today, tomorrow, and every remaining day of your life. Let Him know that His words to you are the joy of your heart.

> *Your statutes are my heritage forever;*
> *they are the joy of my heart.*
> *My heart is set on keeping Your decrees to the very end.*
> Psalm 119:111–112

Today marks the final day of our fast-forward study through the history of Israel. It also marks our final day of focusing the majority of our study in the Old Testament. The second half of this study will be centered on the New Testament, and I'm ready to get there! I love the Old Testament, but it is a record of the Old Covenant (in fact, the word "testament" and "covenant" mean the same thing), and the New Covenant is so much better. And that's not just my opinion, it's a fact. Hebrews 8:6 says that Christ "is the mediator of a better covenant, which has been enacted on better promises" *(NASB)*. Hallelujah, thank you, Jesus!

Our lesson today will cover the temple that was built by the Israelites in Jerusalem *after* their captivity in Babylon. After Babylon was overthrown by the Persians, God stirred the heart of the king of Persia, Cyrus. Under God's prompting, Cyrus encouraged any Israelites who were willing to return to Jerusalem and to build a temple for God (Ezra 1:1–4). A relatively small group returned to Israel under the leadership of Zerubbabel, and they began the work of rebuilding the temple.

Their work, however, was soon hindered by the other nations who lived in the land. Fifteen years later, only the temple's foundation and altar had been completed. Something had to be done. God's temple had to be completed.

Perhaps you're wondering, "What happened?" Excellent question and you'll find the answer yourself as you complete your study today. So open your Bible to the table of contents. Now locate the page number for the tiny Old Testament book of Haggai. When you find Haggai, you'll find your answer—and you'll also find lots of wonderful application for your own life. Enjoy your final day in the Old Testament!

2. The book of Haggai is very brief. Therefore, begin your study by reading through the entire book to familiarize yourself with its message.

3. Summarize the message of the first chapter of Haggai by answering the following questions:

   a. Who is Haggai, and what did he do (v. 1)?

   b. In verses 2 and 4, Haggai very succinctly conveys God's primary problem with the people of Israel. Please review these verses, then complete the following sentences in your own words to paraphrase God's message through Haggai:

      1) The people were saying _____.

      2) But the truth was _____.

   c. What does this reveal about the people's hearts and their relationships with God? What place did God have in their lives?

   d. As a result, what was God allowing to happen to the Israelites (vv. 6, 9–11)?

   e. Think about this question: Have you ever experienced anything like this yourself? If so, please describe how.

   f. What did God command the Israelites to do and why (vv. 8–9)?

    g.   What effect was their negligence having upon God's glory?

4.   How did Zerubbabel and his people respond to God's command, and what does this reveal about their hearts (vv. 12–14)?

5.   Two months later, Haggai spoke again to Zerubbabel and his people. He asked them two questions. Please review Haggai 2:1–3, then answer the following questions:

    a.   What were Haggai's questions and to whom were they directed?

    b.   Why do you think he asked this specific group of people these questions?

    c.   What does this tell you about this temple in comparison with Solomon's temple?

6.   How did God lift their spirits, and what promises did He make to them (Haggai 2: 4–9)?

7.   According to God, what is it that makes the temple glorious, and how does this apply to our own lives (Haggai 2:7)?

8. How would the latter glory of this temple be greater than the former? To discover the answer to this question, please read Luke 2:21–32, and record your answer.

9. Before the temple was completed, God speaks to the people of Israel once again through Haggai. Please read Haggai 2:18–19 and answer the following questions:

    a. What did God promise to do for the people even though the temple was not yet completed?

    b. What does this reveal about God?

10. Now it is time for some very practical application. As you learned, the Israelites were more consumed with their own daily lives and their own well-being than they were with putting God first. What are some of the things that vie for first place in your life? What are some of the things that often threaten to consume you? In my experience, it's not always "bad stuff" that keeps me from putting God first in my life. Often, it's the "good stuff" in my life that overtakes the best. And the best is seeking Christ first and giving Him priority in my life.

    Please complete the following lists by recording some of the "good stuff" and "bad stuff" that prevents you from giving God first place in your life. Be honest. And remember, just as God knew the truth about the people of Israel, He knows the truth about you, too. So follow God's advice to the Israelites, "Give careful thought to your ways" (Haggai 1:5).

The "Good Stuff"	The "Bad Stuff"
_____	_____
_____	_____
_____	_____
_____	_____
_____	_____
_____	_____
_____	_____
_____	_____

The Temple

11. As you conclude this week of study, please do a little journaling in order to reflect back on what God has revealed to you this week. Journal your insights by completing the following sentences:

My Journal

THIS WEEK THE LORD...

_____

_____

_____

_____

_____

_____

_____

_____

AS A RESULT, I...

_____

_____

_____

_____

_____

_____

_____

_____

This week you studied the account of David's journey to Kiriath-jearim to recover the ark of the covenant in order to bring it to Jerusalem. That trip was meticulously designed to be a gigantic parade to welcome the symbol of God's presence (the ark) into Israel's epicenter.

An enormous number of singers, dancers, musicians, and even an entire marching band were handpicked to make the journey with David to Kiriath-jearim. Invitations were issued to priests, dignitaries, and throngs of Israelites. Girl, I'm here to tell you, this event was bigger than a barbeque cook-off in Texas! It was a *big* deal. But as you know, it quickly deteriorated into an even *bigger* disaster.

Not long after the ark was placed on the brand new, first-class (think Cadillac) cart, one of the oxen pulling the cart stumbled. Instinctively but irreverently, Uzzah, one of the Levites, reached out and touched the ark of the covenant in order to steady it—and it was the last thing Uzzah ever did. Immediately God struck him down, and Uzzah died on that very spot. Instantly the parade came to a halt. The crowd was paralyzed with shock. No doubt about it, this party was officially over.

At that point I imagine everyone started backing away very slowly from the Cadillac cart and the killer ark. As the crowd parted, I envision everyone began quietly and cautiously turning their heads in unison to see the response of one man: David. Looking at him, they probably all began wondering the exact, same thing, "What's he gonna do now?" But I think their very next thought was quite possibly, "I hope David doesn't ask me to help with that killer ark."

Massive numbers of people were there that day. Yet even within the enormous crowd, I don't believe one single person volunteered to help. Personally, I think most people probably began crossing their arms, looking down at their feet, doing their utmost to avoid even making eye contact with David. And I certainly don't think anyone was enthusiastically jabbing their hand into the air begging David to, "Pick me, pick me!"

Eventually a decision was made. The ark would be taken to Obed-Edom's house. And then . . . a marvelous and almost miraculous thing happened: *Obed-Edom willingly received the ark into his home and agreed to become its caretaker.* Now I want to ask you something: would *you* have done that? Surely Obed-Edom was aware of the circumstances of the killer ark and of Uzzah's death. He may have even witnessed it.

You won't find very much information about Obed-Edom in the Bible. Unlike David, Obed-Edom doesn't get much ink at all in the Scriptures. Yet even the miniscule amount of information we do know about him speaks volumes. In one solitary verse, 1 Chronicles 13:14, we learn: "The ark of God remained with the family of Obed-Edom in his house for three months, and the Lord blessed his household and everything he had."

Sometimes less really is more. In Obed-Edom's case, the tiny tidbits of knowledge we possess about him simplifies and even emphasizes one single, supernatural truth: *Those who willingly welcome the presence of God into their lives will be blessed.*

Do you long to enjoy the presence and blessing of God in your daily life? Well, my dear sister, you don't have to plan a parade. You don't need a big ol' band. You don't even have to know how to dance—which is very good news to someone like me! The only thing you need to do is to willingly welcome and acknowledge God's awesome presence in your life.

So come on. Right now. Lift your hands to God and enthusiastically say, "Lord, You are welcome in my life. How I long to experience Your blessing. Please, oh, please, pick me! Pick me!"

My sister, Obed-Edom would be *so* proud of you!

The Temple: THE HEART THAT FOLLOWS GOD

Key Principle: *We glorify God in our everyday lives by obediently following Him and by giving Him priority in our hearts.*

Facts About Following God:

Fact #1: God will often call and challenge us to "_____ _____" and _____ _____. *Deut. 1:6–7*

Fact #2: God's _____ will _____ be with us. *Num. 9:15–16*

Fact #3: God's leadership will be _____ and _____. *Num. 9:17*

Fact #4: God will use _____ along our journey to _____ us. *Num. 9:19–22*

Fact #5: God will do _____ _____ before us as we obediently follow Him by faith. *Josh. 3:5, 14–17*

Fact #6: God will _____ those whose lives _____ Him. *1 Sam. 2:27–35*

Fact #7: God requires that we do His _____ His _____. *1 Chron. 13:1–13, 15:12–15*

Fact #8: God requires us to follow Him _____ - _____. *1 Kings 11:1–4, 9, 11*

Fact #9: God requires us to give Him _____ as we follow Him. *Haggai 1:2–4, 8–9*

The Heart That Follows God:

1. Views life on earth as a _____.

2. Continuously _____ and _____ upon God's presence.

3. Watches and waits for His leadership and follows Him _____ and _____ He leads. *Num. 9:23*

4. Allows God to make any _____ _____ to be conformed to the image of Christ.

5. Is _____ and _____.

6. Faithfully_____ God above all others.

7. _____ and _____ seeks to do God's _____ God's _____.

8. Follows God _____-_____.

9. Gives God _____.

God to _____:

"Do not despise these small beginnings, for the Lord rejoices to see the work begin." Zech. 4:10 *NLT*

The Temple: GREATER GLORY

In times past, God's glory dwelt among men in a tent—an *ornate* tent—but a tent nonetheless. That tent was, of course, the Tabernacle. Many years later, Solomon's magnificent Temple replaced the Tabernacle and became the place in which God's glory dwelt. But as the Israelites spiraled downward into sin and idolatry, God's righteous judgment fell upon them. God allowed the Babylonians to pillage, destroy and, ultimately, to burn down the Temple and take the Israelite people into captivity.

Seventy years later, the impoverished exiles of Israel returned to their land and rebuilt the Temple under Zerubbabel's rule. This Temple (often called Zerubbabel's Temple) was erected during a time of great economic depression; it could not even be compared with the ornately embellished, expensively adorned Temple Solomon had built.

But the greatest contrast between Solomon's Temple and Zerubbabel's Temple had nothing to do with the architectural differences or quality of these structures. The greatest contrast was this: Zerubbabel's Temple did not contain the ark of the covenant—there was no *visible* presence of God's glory.* Even still, God reminded the Israelites that His *invisible* presence was with them, and that He was pleased and glorified by their obedience in rebuilding the Temple. God's sweetest encouragement to them, however, was this promise: "The glory of this present house will be greater than the glory of the former house" (Haggai 2:9).

God promised Zerubbabel's temple would one day enjoy far greater glory than even Solomon's spectacular sanctuary. Sure enough, several hundred years later, greater glory came as a carpenter and his young wife entered that temple. In their arms, they held their firstborn—a son. Few recognized God's glory that day as the tiny infant was dedicated. Nevertheless, God had kept His promise. Greater glory had come indeed.

Thus, in between the Old and the New Covenants, God's visible glory came once more and dwelt upon the earth. But it did not come in a cloud or a fiery pillar; it did not reside within a tent or a temple. The glory of God came and dwelt upon the earth in the soft, fragile body of a newborn babe.

This week we'll watch as that baby grows up and glorifies His Father every day of His life. Who better than Christ can teach us the way to glorify God in our everyday lives? No one can, because no one has ever glorified God perfectly except Jesus, God's Son.

Follow Christ closely this week. Observe His example. Allow His Spirit to mold and conform you into His image because Christ has called you to glo, too.

*Note: The ark (and all of the temple furnishings and valuable items it contained) was taken by the Babylonians during their siege and destruction of Jerusalem.

THIS WEEK'S
KEY PRINCIPLE:

*We glorify
God in our
everyday lives
by seeking
to please Him
above all else.*

Day One

1. Here's a great Psalm to begin our week of study. Write the words from this Psalm on a sticky note, and strategically place it where you most need to be reminded of its message—like on your desk at work, or near your kitchen sink where dirty dishes seem to constantly multiply! Begin practicing this scripture right now by praising and glorifying Him in prayer, and don't forget to praise and glorify Him for your job, for dirty dishes, and for all of those other daily blessings in disguise.

    O God, we give glory to You all day long and constantly praise Your name. Psalm 44:8 *NLT*

    Today we will focus on the birth and the early years of Christ. The evidence of God's glory upon His Son was obvious from the very beginning. I think both shepherds and wise men knew this Child would change the world.

2. Luke records the story of Christ's birth, and Matthew records the events that occurred after His birth. Please read both of these passages (listed below) from Luke and Mark. Then under the heading "The Glory of Christ's Birth," please number and list the various ways God displayed and revealed His glory at the time of Christ's birth and in the days that followed.

    a. Luke 2:1–21

    b. Matthew 2:1–15

    ### The Glory of Christ's Birth

    _____

    _____

    _____

    _____

    _____

    _____

    _____

    _____

    _____

    _____

3. Forty days after Jesus' birth, Mary and Joseph took Him to the temple to present Him to the Lord according to the requirements of the law. Before you read any further in this assignment, please read Luke 2:22–38.

As someone who is a weeper (I weep for joy, for sorrow, and for everything in between), I cannot help but think there were some tears flowing in the temple that day. And I believe God wants us to tarry for a few moments and consider this beautiful scene. It is a significant scene, a prophetic scene, a *glorious* scene. Let's not rush.

I want you to imagine that you're Mary or Joseph. You've got one thing in mind as you proceed to the temple: to fulfill the requirement of the law in order to be obedient to God. As you enter the temple area, you notice an elderly man. Instantly, he appears to recognize you—but you don't know him. Hastily he begins making his way across the courtyard toward you. The closer he gets, the more you begin to realize something. It's not *you* he's looking at, as you'd first thought. No, his eyes are completely fixed on the child in your arms.

A brief greeting transpires, "My name is Simeon," and then an anxious, aching question is asked, "May I hold your child?" You trust him. Willingly you transfer your tiny baby into his arms. Then through tears of joy (I think, don't you), the old man begins to rejoice and bless God. His words reveal amazing details about the child you love, yet they also prophesy certain sorrow to come.

At that same moment, before you've even had time to consider fully Simeon's words, an elderly woman—Anna, a prophetess—appears. She joins Simeon in giving thanks to God for sending His Redeemer to His people. After a few minutes, she excuses herself saying, "I cannot keep this good news to myself when so many of us have been waiting and praying for this glad day to come. I must go tell the others."

What a day! Mary and Joseph must have returned to their home saying things like, "I never thought our day would turn out like this." I think Simeon probably went to bed that night with the deepest sense of peace he'd ever experienced. And Anna . . . well, I think she did just what you or I would have done. She spread the word until her voice just flat gave out!

4. As you can see, I think it's very beneficial to visualize scenes from the Scriptures. But now let's take a look at this scene from a different perspective and gain a deeper appreciation for Simeon, his example, and his understanding of Christ. Please refer to Luke 2:22–38 as you record your answers to the following questions:

a. What did you learn about Simeon, and how was he described?

b. What promise had the Holy Spirit given to Simeon?

    c.   What brought him to the temple that day, and how is this similar to the way in which we all "meet" Christ (v. 27)?

    d.   How did he describe Jesus (vv. 32)?

5.   John's gospel does not record the events of the nativity or the dedication at the temple. Yet the Gospel of John beautifully records the incarnation of Christ, the Word. Please record John's words in each of the following references:

    a.   John 1:1

    b.   John 1:4

    c.   John 1:14

6.   Now, please review Simeon's description of Christ and the references from John. Record any comparisons you see.

7.   In the introduction to this lesson, you read Haggai's promise (Haggai 2:9) regarding the greater glory that would one day come to Zerubbabel's temple. You've seen that promise fulfilled as you studied Luke 2. However, another prophet gives us additional information about Christ's visit to the temple. Please read Malachi 3:1, and answer the following questions:

NOTE: The first "messenger" Malachi refers to is John the Baptist, not Christ.

a. As you look closely at this passage, whose temple was it?

b. How is Christ described in this verse?

c. Which covenant is Malachi referring to (if you need help in answering this question, please refer to Hebrews 9:15)?

8. The only other biblical reference to Christ's early years is in the final verses of Luke 2. Complete your study of Jesus' childhood by reading Luke 2:39–52, then answering the following questions:

a. Where did Jesus go when He was twelve years old and why?

b. After Jesus' parents realized He was missing, where specifically did Mary and Joseph find him, and what did Mary say to Jesus? Try to put Mary's words into the modern-day language of an everyday mom.

c. Record word-for-word Jesus' response to His mother.

d. The words you just wrote are the first recorded words of Christ. Think about it: Why are these words so significant? What do they reveal about Jesus as a child? Please record your insights.

e. What further information does this passage reveal about Jesus (vv. 51–52)?

A babe. A mother's son. A twelve-year-old boy. Yet Jesus was also the Word, the light, the glory of the Father, the messenger of the covenant and *so much more.*

9. As you ponder what you've studied today, what insights has the Lord given you, and what is your response to what you've learned? Please briefly journal your answers to these questions.

_____

_____

_____

_____

_____

_____

_____

_____

Day Two

1. It is only by God's mercy that we can draw near to Him. Approach Him today reverently, and humble yourself before Him—perhaps even on your knees—as you spend time with Him in prayer.

But I, by Your great mercy, will come into Your house;
in reverence will I bow down toward Your holy temple.
Psalm 5:7

Yesterday you studied the birth and childhood of Christ. Between the ages of twelve and thirty, the scriptures are silent about Christ's life. The only information we have is found at the conclusion of the Luke 2: "And Jesus grew in wisdom and stature, and in favor with God and men" (Luke 2:52).

Eighteen years of silence will end as Jesus begins His brief, earthly ministry. Yet in this span of three short years, Jesus will accomplish more than any other person, group, or nation ever has or ever will.

2. In light of what we have previously studied about the Old Covenant tabernacle and the glory of the Old Covenant, we need to "camp out" (pardon the tabernacle pun) in a verse you briefly studied yesterday:

> *The Word became flesh and made His dwelling among us. We have seen His glory, the glory of the One and Only, who came from the Father, full of grace and truth.*
>
> —John 1:14

Using John 1:14, please answer the following questions:

a. Who is the Word and what did He do?

b. What did others witness through His life?

The word "dwelling" in John 1:14 is especially significant for us. In the Greek, this word means "to encamp, pitch a tent…to dwell as in tents, to tabernacle."[1] Once again we see the beauty and symbolism of the Old Testament tabernacle as it foreshadowed Christ who came to earth, pitched His tent, and "tabernacled" among men.

Imagine the condescension of Christ, leaving the courts of heaven to dwell among sinful men, enabling them not only to witness but also to partake in His glory!

My sister, what I am about to say is very important in our understanding of this study. I hope I've made myself clear thus far but, just in case I haven't, please allow me to clarify myself. In the first half of this study of *The Temple*, we learned that the glory of God's presence dwelt within the tabernacle and in the temple under the Old Covenant system. Even the visible glory on Moses' face was temporary and pointed to a future time when God's glory would inhabit His children permanently (2 Corinthians 3:7–18). As we begin this second half of *The Temple*, these are the primary points we need to understand:

Jesus came to:

- **Fulfill the Law through His sinless life and perfect sacrifice.** Everything in the Old Covenant found its completion in Christ. No more tents, no more temples, no more clouds or pillars of fire, no more sacrifices are necessary. (Hebrews 9)
- **Reveal God's glory "in the flesh" to sinful men.**
- **Introduce and inaugurate the New Covenant by His death and resurrection.**
- **Enable us to become living, breathing temples of God so that we can reflect His glory through our everyday lives.**

Without Jesus our lives would be empty and vain. But because of Him we can experience fulfillment and eternal significance. Hallelujah!

Now, let's return to John 1:14 and take a closer look at the word "glory." Glory is the Greek word *doxa*. In our first week of study together, we learned that God's glory refers to His divine nature and attributes.[2] As we begin our study of Christ, I want to give you some additional information about the meaning of *doxa*. In *The Complete Word Study Dictionary, doxa* or glory is described as "the true apprehension of God … Giving glory to God is ascribing to Him His full recognition."[3]

Jesus certainly had a "true apprehension"[4] of God because Jesus was God in the flesh. John said it best, "In the beginning was the Word, and the Word was with God, and the Word was God" (John 1:1). And because He was God in the flesh, Jesus was able to glorify God fully and perfectly.

For the remainder of your study today, you'll be observing the beginning of Jesus' public, earthly ministry to see the ways in which He glorified God. Personally, I think it's interesting that Jesus' public ministry didn't begin with a big speech or a publicity campaign announcing, "Here He is. Your long-awaited Messiah has finally come!" In fact, Jesus didn't even begin His ministry by preaching an impressive sermon at the local synagogue. Instead, Jesus chose to begin His ministry in a very symbolic, deeply significant way and, oh, how God was glorified!

3. To discover how Jesus' public ministry began, please read Matthew 3:13–17.

   a. Describe your own thoughts about the significance and symbolism of the way He chose to begin His public ministry and how it glorified God.

   b. As we seek to fulfill God's plan for our lives and minister to others, what can we learn from Jesus' example?

4. Please read John 1:17–34, and answer the following questions:

    a.   How did John describe Jesus' ministry as opposed to the law (the Old Covenant)?

    b.   Because Jesus "tabernacled" on earth, what was He able to reveal or to explain through His life and ministry (v. 18)?

    c.   How did John describe Christ? Make a list as you refer to verses 29–34.

    d.   What supernatural event occurred at Jesus' baptism that bore witness to the fact that Jesus was God's Son?

5. Luke 4 records the event that followed Christ's baptism. Please read Luke 4:1–13, then answer the following questions:

    a.   Why did Jesus immediately go to the wilderness after His baptism?

    b.   What does this reveal about the Holy Spirit?

    c.   What does this teach you about some of your own "wilderness" experiences?

d. Why do you think the baptism of Christ is immediately followed by the temptation of Christ in the wilderness? In other words, why didn't God just allow Jesus to begin publicly preaching and healing immediately following His baptism?

e As believers, what application does the previous question have for us?

6. Printed below is Luke 4:6. Please read this verse, and answer the questions that follow.

The Devil told him, "I will give You the glory of these kingdoms and authority over them—because they are mine to give to anyone I please."

—Luke 4:6 *NLT*

a. What did Satan promise to give to Jesus?

b. How does Satan also tempt us in this way?

c. How did Jesus glorify God during the temptation (you may want to review Luke 4:1–12)?

7. It's honesty time, dear sister. Satan's tactics haven't changed through the centuries. In your own life—in recent days or in the past—how has Satan tempted you by promising to give you glory and authority?

_____

_____

_____

_____

_____

_____

_____

_____

— ✦ *Day Three* ✦ —

1. Begin your day of study in prayer. But before you utter a single word to the Lord, spend a few moments meditating on His great love for you.

Within Your temple, O God,
we meditate on Your unfailing love. Psalm 48:9

Amazing, isn't it, how quickly a day can go from good to bad? Sure we may have some prolonged periods of ease with very few problems and relatively little strife, but that's not the norm. Most of our days are a combination of both good and bad, high and low.

My sister, if we're ever going to learn how to glorify God in our everyday lives, we must learn how to handle the highs and lows of everyday life. Today you will study some of the highs and lows of Jesus' life and ministry. Observe how He glorifies God in good days and in not-so-good days. Trust me, this is a lesson you will have the opportunity to apply very soon!

2. Jesus performed many miracles during His earthly ministry. But not everyone viewed these miracles in a positive way. Many times Jesus' miracles produced both positive and negative responses. Please complete the following chart by:

- Reading the scriptures listed (in column one),

- Recording a brief description of the miracle under the scripture reference (in column one),

- Recording a summary of what happened as a result of this miracle placing a positive mark (+) beside the positive results/response and a negative (-) mark beside the negative results/response (in column two), and

- Recording what that miracle revealed about Christ (in column three).

Miracles: The Positives and The Negatives		
Scripture/ Miracle	Summary of Results	Revelation About Christ
Luke 5:17–26		
Luke 13:10–17		
John 9:1–38		
John 11:1–46		

3. In the early part of Jesus' earthly ministry, after He had performed miracles in other cities, He returned to His hometown of Nazareth where He had grown up. As you continue to study the highs and lows of Jesus' earthly ministry, please read the account of Jesus' time in Nazareth in Luke 4:16–30. Summarize what happened to Him in His hometown, noting especially the highs and the lows of this specific day of His life.

4. How did Jesus consistently glorify God throughout the highs and lows of His earthly ministry?

5. Experiencing any highs and lows in your life? Please record some of them on the following chart:

My Highs	My Lows

6. What characteristics in Jesus' life do you need to develop as you face the everyday highs and lows of your life? After recording your insights, take a few moments to take all of this before your merciful Father in heaven. Confess your shortcomings as well as your needs to Him, and remember:

> *For we do not have a high priest who is unable to sympathize with our weaknesses, but we have One who has been tempted in every way, just as we are—yet was without sin. Let us then approach the throne of grace with confidence, so that we may receive mercy and find grace to help us in our time of need.*
> —Hebrews 4:15–16

_____

_____

_____

_____

_____

_____

_____

_____

_____

Day Four

1. As you begin your time of study in prayer, ask God to speak to your heart today. And by the way, aren't you grateful that our Father not only hears us, but that He also answers us? Don't allow anything to drown out His sweet voice, my sister.

    Right now I have a habit the Lord is exhorting me to break. When I get into my car, I automatically turn on the radio or a CD. But lately when I reach to push the "on" switch, He's prompting me to ask Him whether or not I should turn it on or leave it off. As a result, my errands and car trips are increasingly becoming wonderful times of fellowship and praise to the Father. So if you live in a noisy world like I do, here's a little tip: Quiet. Try it.

> *To the Lord I cry aloud,*
> *and He answers me from His holy hill.* Psalm 3:4

Before you begin your study today, let me give you some background information about the temple that stood during Jesus' day.

As you learned in Week Five, Zerubbabel's temple was constructed by the Jewish exiles after they had returned to Jerusalem following their captivity in Babylon. This temple was not as beautiful as Solomon's temple had been, yet God promised greater glory would one day come to Zerubbabel's temple. This glory, as you know, initially arrived when Jesus' earthly parents brought Him to the temple to be dedicated. During Jesus' public ministry, greater glory returned many more times as Jesus taught at the temple when He came to Jerusalem to celebrate the Jewish festivals.

After Zerubbabel's temple was constructed, Jerusalem was besieged and assaulted numerous times throughout the years by enemy armies, and the temple was pillaged and desecrated many times as well. In 67 BC, however, Roman rule was established in Jerusalem; and in 37 BC Herod became king of Jerusalem.

In order to gain favor with the Jewish people, Herod began the process of restoring and reconstructing Zerubbabel's temple. Under Herod's rule the temple was not only restored, it was also much improved in beauty and adornment, and the entire temple area was greatly enlarged. As a result, the temple during Jesus' day became known as "Herod's Temple."

Herod's Temple was the jewel of Jerusalem and the Jewish people were very proud of it. But you know what the Bible says about pride: "Pride goes before destruction, a haughty spirit before a fall" (Proverbs 16:18). In your study today, you'll see the early evidences of this pride.

2. Today your study will center on what Christ taught about the temple. Please begin by reading John 2:11–22. Then answer the following questions:

a. As you look at the context of this account, what event immediately preceded it?

b. When did Jesus first cleanse the temple? Place a check in the box beside the correct answer.

- ❑ before His public ministry began
- ❑ early in His public ministry
- ❑ in the final days of His public ministry

c.   Where was the temple located, and why did Jesus go there?

d.   At the temple, why did Jesus become angry, and what did He do?

e.   How did Jesus refer to the temple? In other words, what did He call it?

f.   What response did Jesus receive from the Jews, and how did He respond to them?

g.   What did Jesus mean by His response?

3.   Mark 11 records another similar scene during Jesus' public ministry. Please scan Mark 11:1–10 and read Mark 11:15–18; then answer the following questions:

a.   When did this cleansing of the temple take place? Please place a check in the box beside the correct answer.

☐   early in His public ministry
☐   in the midpoint of His public ministry
☐   in the final days of His public ministry

b.   How did Jesus refer to the temple in this passage? In other words, what did He call it?

     c.   How did the priests respond to Jesus' cleansing of the temple?

     d.   What do these two accounts reveal about temple worship and the priesthood during Jesus' life?

4.   Please read Mark 13:1–2 and Luke 19:43–44, and record what Jesus foretold about the temple's future.

5.   Earlier in His ministry, Jesus had a conversation with a woman of Samaria. In it the woman asked Jesus several questions about religion and worship. Please read this account in John 4:20–24 and answer the following questions:

     a.   What was the Samaritan woman seeking to clarify in verse 20?

     b.   What did Jesus prophesy and teach her about future worship and the place of true worship?

Finally, let me give you your last history lesson regarding the temple. After Christ's death, the prophecy He made regarding the temple was fulfilled. In 70 AD the Romans stormed Jerusalem, set fire to Herod's Temple, and destroyed it completely. Since that time a Jewish temple has never been rebuilt.

Instead, in the seventh century, another structure was erected on the former temple site. This structure is the Mosque of Omar, more commonly referred to as "The Dome of the Rock." It was built by the Muslims to commemorate their prophet, Muhammad. Tragically the large gold dome of a false religion has now become the dominant feature of Jerusalem's landscape.

You may be wondering, "Will another temple ever be built?" Yes, the scriptures teach there will be a temple during the millennial reign of Christ and that the nations will come and worship there (Isaiah 2:2–4, Ezekiel 40–43, Zechariah 14).

Until then, however, let me remind you of our key passage for this study:

> *Or do you not know that your body is a temple of the Holy Spirit who is in you, whom you have from God, and that you are not your own? For you have been bought with a price: therefore glorify God in your body.*
>
> —1 Corinthians 6:19–20 *NASB*

6. Matthew 12:1–8 records a confrontation between Jesus and the Pharisees. Please read this passage and record what Jesus revealed about His relationship with the Old Covenant Law and the temple. Also, how did He describe Himself in verse 8?

7. God's temple today is the individual body of every believer and the corporate body of the church. Sister, until we see Christ—whether by rapture or by death—we've got a job to do. By now you should know what I'm about to say but, this time, I want *you* to say it! So please record what God has called us, as His temples, to do by filling in the following blanks:

You _____, _____!

8. How has the Lord spoken to your heart today? Please record your insights.

_____

_____

_____

_____

_____

_____

_____

_____

Day Five

1. Did you know God loves the sound of your voice, and He especially loves to hear you sing? Today, after you've spent some time in prayer, conclude your prayer with a solo of praise to the Lord. Sing any hymn or praise song the Holy Spirit impresses upon your heart. And don't worry about how you think your voice sounds. Just make His praise *glo*.

Sing the glory of His name;
make His praise glorious! Psalm 66:2

Since you just completed your musical solo for God's ears, I have a message I trust will be music to *your* ears: Today your study will be brief. Precious sister, you've poured over the Scriptures diligently this week, and I so appreciate your dedication to the mandate of 2 Timothy 2:15: "Be diligent to present yourself approved to God as a workman who does not need to be ashamed, handling accurately the word of truth."

Enjoy your final day of study this week. And feel free to hum or sing—or even whistle—while you work. Give Him glory—keep glo-ing!

2. There are many ways we can glorify God in our everyday lives. As you read each of the following scriptures, record what they teach about how to glorify God.

    a.   Matthew 5:16

    b.   Luke 17:11–18

    c.   John 11:1–4

    d.   John 14:13

    e.   John 15:5–8

3. Take a few minutes now to reflect upon all you've studied this week and the way the Lord has spoken to you. Then freely journal your thoughts and insights below.

My Journal

THIS WEEK THE LORD...

_____

_____

_____

_____

_____

_____

_____

_____

_____

_____

AS A RESULT, I...

_____

_____

_____

_____

_____

_____

_____

_____

_____

_____

_____

One of the things I am most grateful to the Lord for is that I grew up constantly hearing and listening to gospel music. My daddy (John McKay) is a gospel singer and musician who led music in churches and revival meetings all over the country. There was always music in our house, in our cars, and everywhere we went—and I do mean *everywhere*.

I vividly remember going shopping at the mall with my dad when I was a teenager. He has always been so much fun on any kind of shopping trip—I've never met a man who enjoys running errands and even grocery shopping as much as he does! But I digress . . . back to the mall. As we'd walk down the long, wide corridors of the mall, my dad would often begin singing. He didn't sing loudly, and he certainly wasn't performing. In fact, most of the time, he was completely unaware of the audible sounds that were coming from his lips.

As a teenager, that used to embarrass me. I would begin looking around to see if others could hear him—they *could*—and I'm ashamed to tell you that I would often look at him and, in the annoyed tone of a teenager, I'd say, "Da-*uhd*." In mid-note he'd catch himself and stop singing—for the time being. But eventually he would unconsciously tune up again. He just couldn't seem to help it.

Dad is in his seventies now, and he hasn't changed one bit—and I'm so glad. And since I've grown up I now not only understand, but I also deeply admire the constant song on his lips. You see, those unconscious melodies are really just the overflow of the ongoing song within his heart.

When I think about my daddy, I always think about this verse: "Be filled with the Spirit. Speak to one another with psalms, hymns and spiritual songs. Sing and make music in your heart to the Lord" (Ephesians 5:18–19).

Sister, let's do something. Let's *sing*. Let's give expression to the song He has placed within our hearts. In our cars, in the aisles of the grocery store, and especially in our homes, let's sing. Audibly or inaudibly. Consciously or unconsciously. As the Spirit leads you, sing. Sure, you may occasionally annoy a teenager, and you may even experience the stares of strangers. But you will also glorify God. And never forget: as His temple, that's what you're here for. So *sing*, and you're sure to start glo-ing, girl!

The Temple: THE 4 CHARACTERISTICS OF GOD PLEASERS

<u>*Key Principle:*</u> *We glorify God in our everyday lives*
by seeking to please God above all else.

The 3 primary choices of everyday life:

1. _____-pleaser: the choice to _____ _____ above everyone and everything else.

2. _____-pleaser: the choice to _____ _____ above God and everything else.

3. _____-pleaser: the choice to _____ _____ above everyone and everything else.

"But passing through their midst, (Jesus) went _____ _____." Luke 4:30

The woman who pleases God will possess these 4 characteristics:

1. The _____: *Isaiah 50:5–7, Mark 1:38, Luke 4:42–43, Mark 14:36*

   You must **know**: Your call is to _____ _____.

   You must **practice**: _____ _____ no matter the cost.

2. The _____: *John 8:31–32, Matthew 7:24–25*

   You must **know**: What you _____, and your _____ must be based upon the _____ of God's Word.

   You must **practice**: Making everyday _____ based upon the _____ of God's Word.

3. The _____: *Mark 2:3–12, 15–17, 23–27, 4:36–39*

   You must **know**: You will be _____ and _____.

   You must **practice**: Standing firmly in the _____ and _____ _____ in love to others.

4. The _____: *Mark 6:34, 8:1–2*

   You must **know**: The two-fold _____ for ministry: 1) _____ for God, and 2) _____ for others.

   You must **practice**: The priorities of _____ and _____ God first, and _____ and _____ others as a result.

"It's your choice: Will you choose God's way for _____ life?

The Temple: THE GLORY OF THE CROSS

Last week we studied the glory of Christ's birth and childhood, the glory of His sinless life, and the glory of His earthly ministry and miracles. Imagine being among the shepherds who witnessed the glorious pronouncement of His birth:

> *An angel of the Lord appeared to them, and the glory of the Lord shone around them. ...Suddenly a great company of the heavenly host appeared with the angel, praising God and saying "Glory to God in the highest, and on earth peace to men on whom His favor rests."*
>
> —Luke 2:9–14

Or envision being one of the Jewish teachers who conversed with Jesus at the temple when He was only a child. All who saw and heard him that day witnessed the glory of God embodied in a 12-year-old boy, and the Scripture tells us that:

> *Everyone who heard Him was amazed at His understanding and His answers.*
>
> —Luke 2:47

And can you imagine being inside the packed house of people who were listening to Christ teach when the roof suddenly broke open and a paralytic man was lowered into the room on a stretcher? Everyone present witnessed God's glory as Jesus healed the broken man as evidenced by their response:

> *They were all seized with astonishment and began glorifying God and they were filled with fear, saying, "We have seen remarkable things today."*
>
> —Luke 5:26 NASB

From His birth, through His childhood, in His ministry, and through His miracles, Jesus consistently glorified God every day of His life. Yet even still, I believe Jesus' greatest glory was witnessed not through His *life*—but through His *death*.

The glory of the cross. Think about it. Without the cross there would be no redemption. Without the cross there would be no resurrection. Without the cross we would forever "fall short of the glory of God" (Romans 3:23). There's glory in the cross.

Precious sister, just think: One day we, too, will be eyewitnesses of Christ's glory. Imagine what *that* day is going to be like! But until the trumpet sounds and we meet Him in the air, or until by death we are absent from the body and at home with the Lord, may the glorious results of the cross be visible in our everyday lives as we take up our cross and *glo!*

THIS WEEK'S
KEY PRINCIPLE:

We glorify God in our everyday lives by responding to persecution and suffering as Christ did.

Day One

1. As I write this study, a war is raging in Iraq and the stability of the rest of the world is threatened by terrorism. Perhaps by the time you're doing this study the world situation will have changed—but I doubt that it has changed very much. In war and in peace, in days of stability and instability, aren't you glad we can rest in the truth of today's Psalm? Praise Him today for His majesty and glory in all the earth as you begin your time of study in prayer.

> O Lord, our Lord,
> how majestic is Your name in all the earth!
> You have set Your glory above the heavens. Psalm 8:1

Several weeks ago you vicariously climbed Mount Sinai with Moses to see the glory of God. Today you'll climb another mountain: the Mount of Transfiguration. On this mountain you'll see Jesus in all of His glory. This miraculous experience, however, will mark a significant turning point in Christ's ministry because as He descends from the Mount of Transfiguration, Jesus will begin His final journey to another, very different mountain: Mount Calvary.

2. In order for you to appreciate fully the experience on the Mount of Transfiguration, please read Luke 9:18–27 which records Jesus' words to His disciples just a few days prior to His transfiguration. After you've read this passage, please answer the following questions:

   a. What does Jesus reveal to His disciples in verse 22? Record your answer by completing the following sentence:

   The Son of Man must _____

   _____

   _____.

   b. After revealing what is about to happen to Him, Jesus lists the requirements for following Him (vv. 23–24). Please record these requirements.

   c. What does verse 22 have in common with verses 23–24? In other words, how does Jesus' revelation of what is about to happen to Him parallel with the requirements of being a disciple?

d.   What does this reveal to you about your own walk with Christ?

e.   What does Jesus reveal about Himself and the future in verse 26?

The passage you've just read from Luke 9 records the very first time Jesus ever told His disciples about His approaching death. He is about to begin the final days of His earthly ministry, and Jesus is preparing them for His crucifixion.

Eight days later, Jesus invites three of His disciples (Peter, James, and John) to a mountain to pray with Him. As they climb the mount with Christ, they have no clue of the glorious climax ahead of them. Soon they will see the supernatural as Jesus is transformed—glorified—before their very eyes. Let's follow along and take this journey with them!

3. Please read Luke 9:28–36 picturing this passage in your mind as you read. Now I'd like for you to try and recapture this experience from Peter's point of view. How do you think he would describe what he saw and heard that night? How did this experience possibly affect him? Put yourself in Peter's shoes and use your imagination as you complete his journal page (I've given you a little introduction to help you get started).

> *Only eight days ago, Jesus began teaching us some challenging and troubling truths. Something new seemed to be stirring deep within Him. I didn't understand it then, and I don't fully understand it even now. But after what I witnessed last night, I am most confident of this: my commitment to Him is complete.*
>
> *Yesterday Jesus invited John, James, and me to ascend a mountain to spend time with Him in prayer. It was a very long climb. I must have been extremely exhausted because I fell asleep praying. I have no idea how long I was asleep, but when I woke up…*

_____

_____

_____

_____

_____

_____

4. Moses and Elijah are much-revered Old Testament figures. On the Mount of Transfiguration, Moses represented the Old Covenant Law, and Elijah represented the Old Testament prophets. Jesus represents the fulfillment of both the Old Covenant Law and the prophecies of the Old Testament prophets. What were they discussing with Jesus during the transfiguration?

5. As you consider what Jesus was discussing with Moses and Elijah, why was Peter's desire (to build three tabernacles and remain on the mountain) not only impossible, but also inappropriate? What does this reveal about Peter?

6. The word "transfigured" is the Greek word *metamorphoo* from which we get our English word *metamorphosis*. This word is used in only two other New Testament passages. Each time *metamorphoo* is translated *transformed*. Please read these two passages, and record what you learn from them and how it relates to us today.

   a. Romans 12:1–2

   b. 2 Corinthians 3:16–18

7. After Jesus' death, resurrection and ascension, Peter wrote the books of 1 and 2 Peter. In 2 Peter he refers to his experience on the Mount of Transfiguration. Please read 2 Peter 1:16–21, and record why the transfiguration was so important to him and to the other New Testament writers.

8. Conclude your day of study by recording any insights the Holy Spirit has given you. Also, please record how you have experienced transformation in your life.

_____

_____

_____

_____

_____

_____

_____

_____

— *Day Two* —

1. As you read today's Psalm, I'd like for you to underline the two phrases that begin with the words "He will." After you've done that, take a moment to re-read this verse allowing the truth of that tiny two-word phrase to spiritually sink in. Now I want to ask you a question: What trouble, what problem, what stressful situation are you facing today? Prayerfully pour your situation out before God, then place your faith in His promise to you today.

For in the day of trouble He will keep me safe in His dwelling;
He will hide me in the shelter of His tabernacle
and set me high upon a rock. Psalm 27:5

Our study today will focus on several key events that precede Jesus' death. I have simplified today's homework as much as possible in a desire to help you focus singularly upon Jesus as He willingly, steadfastly follows the path to the cross.

Watch Him closely. Learn from His example. And remember He—like no one else—models for us what it truly means to glorify God.

2. Begin today's study by reading through John 11, underlining the words "glory" or "glorified" each time they are used. As you read, also observe:

   • how Jesus glorifies God, and
   • what Jesus teaches about the glory of God and glorifying God.

After you've finished reading John 11, please answer the questions on the following chart:

What was the purpose of Lazarus' illness and death?
What did the miracle of Lazarus' resurrection reveal and prove about Christ? What did Jesus teach about God's glory?
What were the results (both good and bad) of Lazarus' resurrection?
If possible, briefly describe a time when you witnessed God's glory through illness or death.

3. Please read John 12:1–28, underlining the words "glory" or "glorified" each time they are used. As you read, also observe:

   • how Jesus is worshipped or receives glory from others, and
   • what Jesus teaches about the glory of God and glorifying God.

After you've finished reading this passage from John 12, please answer the questions on the following chart:

How did others worship or glorify Jesus?
What did you learn about the disciples and their understanding of Christ's life and death?
As you look at verses 23 and 27, what "hour" was Jesus referring to, and in what way would He and the Father be glorified?
What principles did Jesus teach us about glorifying God (vv. 23–28)?
How did Jesus model these principles?
What did you learn about Christ's emotions as He faced the hour of His death, and what does this mean in your own life (v. 27)?

4. Take another look at John 12:24–26. How can you practically apply these principles to your everyday life? In other words, what opportunities do you have to practice these principles right now?

5. As you've read, Mary (Lazarus' sister) loved Jesus immensely. It is often noted that every time she is mentioned in Scripture, Mary is worshipping at Jesus' feet. Based upon what you read about Mary in John 12:1–8, please thoughtfully consider the questions below and record your answers:

   a. Beyond her obvious love for Jesus, what else do Mary's actions reveal about her and about her relationship with Christ?

   b. What can we learn from Mary's example as we seek to glorify the Lord?

   c. What did you learn from Mary's example about the cost of glorifying Christ?

6. In what specific ways is the Spirit leading you to follow Mary's example? Prayerfully, carefully consider this question before recording your answer.

_____

_____

_____

_____

_____

_____

_____

— ❧ *Day Three* ❧ —

1. Look closely at today's Psalm. Do you see it? The Psalmist is talking to himself—in a very healthy way, of course. Actually he's asking himself a couple of questions—really *good* questions. Then he gives himself some excellent advice and reminds himself of the hope and help he has in God. Sister, maybe you need to have a little question and answer session with yourself today. Ask yourself, "Why am I worrying today? Why have I become upset and fearful?" Then activate your faith by believing and praising the Lord for His hope, His help, and His presence in your life.

> *Why are you in despair, O my soul?*
> *And why have you become disturbed within me?*
> *Hope in God, for I shall again praise Him*
> *for the help of His presence.* Psalm 42:5 *NASB*

Today and tomorrow you'll study Jesus' final hours with His disciples just prior to His betrayal and arrest. Jesus knows this will be His last night with them. He knows these will be His last words to them. It would not be an overstatement to say that this particular night will be His most important night with them. So during these monumental minutes, He will prepare them. He will pray for them. And on the following day…He will die for them.

2. Please read John 13:1–17, and answer the following questions:

   a. According to verses 1–3, what does Jesus know as He begins His final evening with His disciples? Please record your answers in the following blanks:

   Jesus Knows:

   1. v. 1   His _____ has come and He will soon
      _____.

   2. v. 3a   The Father has _____
      _____.

   3. v. 3b   That He had _____.

   4. v. 3c   That He was _____.

   b. In light of all that Jesus knew, what was the first thing He did that night, and *why* did He do it? Please answer this question by underlining your answers in the following scriptures:

   > *It was just before the Passover Feast. Jesus knew that the time had come for Him to leave this world and go to the Father, having loved His own who were in the world, He now showed them the full extent of His love.*
   >
   > —John 13:1

So He got up from the meal, took off His outer clothing, and wrapped a towel around His waist. After that, He poured water into a basin and began to wash His disciples' feet, drying them with the towel that was wrapped around Him.

—John 13:4–5

c. How did this demonstrate Jesus' love for His disciples?

d. As you look at this passage, what is the relationship between love and servanthood?

e. Jesus glorified God in everything that He did. As you look at His example in this passage, in what specific way is He teaching us to glorify God in our everyday lives?

3. The next event in Jesus' final night with His disciples is the Last Supper. Please read Matthew 26:26–29, and answer the following questions:

a. How did Jesus describe the significance of the wine they shared that night? What did it symbolize and represent?

b. According to this passage, why was the shed blood of Christ necessary?

4. Please read the following verse and circle what the Old Covenant and the New Covenant (the covenant Jesus spoke of in Matthew 26) have in common:

Moses then took the blood, sprinkled it on the people and said, "This is the blood of the covenant that the LORD has made with you in accordance with all these words."

—Exodus 24:8

5. In the first half of our study of *The Temple*, we focused on the Old Covenant (the Law), and we saw the glory of the Tabernacle and the glory of the Temple. But Hebrews 7:22 says, "Jesus has become the guarantee of a better covenant." In what ways is the New Covenant better than the Old Covenant? To discover the answer to this question, please read Hebrews 10:1–22. Then complete the following lists by contrasting the Old Covenant with the New Covenant. I'll help you by starting these lists for you.

Why the New Covenant is better than the Old Covenant	
The Old Covenant	**The New Covenant**
1. v. 1 was only a shadow of the New Covt.	*1. v. 5–7 was the sacrifice of Christ's body*
2. v. 2 its sacrifices could never perfectly cleanse people from sin	

6. How I pray that your study today has resulted in a deeper appreciation for all Christ has done for you. What have you learned today from Christ's example? How is He leading you to apply what you've learned today to your life? Briefly journal your insights to these questions.

Insights

_____

_____

_____

_____

_____

_____

_____

_____

_____

_____

Day Four

1. Exalt Him today in enthusiastic prayer just as the Psalmist models for us. Let Him know how much you long to reflect His glory as you sojourn here on Planet Earth.

    Be exalted, O God, above the highest heavens!
    May Your glory shine over all the earth. Psalm 57:5 *NLT*

    Today you'll continue your study of Jesus' final hours with His disciples. Keep in mind that Jesus is trying to prepare them for the days ahead. And as you see Him praying for them, pay close attention because He is not just praying for *them*. On the night before His death, Jesus prayed for you, too. And glory—what a prayer it was!

2. After the Last Supper, Jesus begins teaching His disciples about the Holy Spirit. Before you study Jesus' words to His disciples, please read Ezekiel 36:26–27. This passage is a prophecy that describes the New Covenant. Please record all that you learn about the Holy Spirit.

3. Read the following scriptures and record what Jesus taught His disciples about the Holy Spirit:

    a. John 14:16–20

    b. John 14:26

c.   John 15:26–27

d.   John 16:8–15

4. In order to gain a greater understanding of the Holy Spirit, please read
    Romans 8:1–17. Then answer the following questions:

    a.   According to verse 4, how are we to walk/live?

    b.   Using the principles from verses 5–8, please describe in your own words
         the difference between the mindset of the Christian and the mindset of
         the non-Christian.

    c.   What significant truth is taught in verse 9?

    d.   According to verses 10–13, what does the indwelling of the Holy Spirit
         give us the power to do in our daily life?

    e.   According to verses 14–17, what are some of the marks of a true Christian?

5. As you consider all you've studied today about the Holy Spirit, please note a few of the ways you have seen the Spirit at work in your life recently.

6. John 17 is often referred to as the high priestly prayer of Jesus. This prayer followed Jesus' final teachings to His disciples. Read John 17 and:
   - Underline every mention of the words "glory," "glorify," or "glorified."
   - Notice who Christ is praying for and the purpose of His prayer.
   - Record your answers to the questions that follow.

   a. How does Christ pray for Himself?

   b. How does Christ pray for His disciples?

   c. How does Christ pray for us, His church?

   d. What did you learn about glory and glorifying God?

7. One of the requests of Jesus' high priestly prayer is that we be in unity and oneness with other Christians. Are any of your Christian relationships strained? If so, read the following scriptures and take time to pray about these relationships. Be sensitive to the leadership of the Holy Spirit, and commit to follow through in any and every way He leads you.

> *Therefore, if you are offering your gift at the altar and there remember that your brother has something against you leave your gift there in front of the altar. First go and be reconciled to your brother; then come and offer your gift.*
>
> —Matthew 5:23–24

> *For if you forgive men when they sin against you, your heavenly Father will also forgive you. But if you do not forgive men their sins, your Father will not forgive your sins.*
>
> —Matthew 6:14–15

> *If it is possible, as far as it depends on you live at peace with everyone.*
> —Romans 12:18

> *And do not grieve the Holy Spirit of God, with whom you were sealed for the day of redemption. Get rid of all bitterness, rage and anger, brawling and slander, along with every form of malice. Be kind and compassionate to one another, forgiving each other, just as in Christ God forgave you.*
>
> —Ephesians 4:30–32

8. How has the Holy Spirit spoken to you today? Please record your insights.

_____

_____

_____

_____

_____

_____

_____

_____

Insights

The Temple

Day Five

1. Notice where today's Psalm was sung. As God's temple, please take a few moments to praise and thank Him for rescuing you from your sin and for refusing to let your enemy, Satan, triumph over you. Dedicate yourself today for His glory.

> *A psalm of David, sung at the dedication of the Temple.*
> *"I will praise You, LORD, for You have rescued me.*
> *You refused to let my enemies triumph over me."*
> Psalm 30:1 *NLT*

Today you will conclude your study of Christ by focusing on His death *and* resurrection. You are about to see that Christ's suffering resulted in His victory and *ours*. Glory!

2. Please read John 12:27–32, and record what you learn about Christ's purpose and the purpose of the cross.

3. Now slowly and reverently, please read John 19. As you read, picture yourself standing at the foot of the cross. After you've finished reading, please spend a few moments on your knees thanking and praising Him for laying down His life for you.

4. Why was it necessary for Christ to suffer? Please read the following passages and record what you learn:

   a. Hebrews 2:9–10

   b. Hebrews 2:14–18

   c. 1 Peter 2:21–24

5. There are many scriptures we could study about suffering, but please simply read 1 Peter 4:12–19. Then compile a list of what you learn from this passage about how to respond to suffering.

How To Respond to Suffering

_____

_____

_____

_____

_____

_____

_____

_____

6. As you look at the list you just made, and as you think about the difficult circumstances you've faced in the past or are facing now, how is the Spirit leading you to respond to suffering in your life?

7. After Christ's resurrection, He appeared many times before His disciples and followers prior to His ascension. Please read Luke 24:36–49, and answer the following questions:

   a. What did you learn about Jesus' glorified body?

   b. Why did Jesus have to suffer and die?

   c. What instructions did Jesus give to His followers?

8. Please read Acts 1:1–11, and answer the following questions:

   a. What promise did Christ instruct His followers to wait for in Jerusalem (vv. 4–5)?

   b. What would the result of this promise be (v. 8)?

   c. After Christ's ascension, what promise was given to His followers?

9. My sister, I know God is going to bless you for all the time you've spent in His Word. If you have time, please conclude your week of study by journaling what the Lord has done in your life this week and how you will respond to all that He's shown you.

My Journal

THIS WEEK THE LORD…

_____

_____

_____

_____

_____

_____

AS A RESULT, I…

_____

_____

_____

_____

_____

_____

_____

Don't you just love the Apostle Peter? I do, and this week you saw him in fine form on the Mount of Transfiguration. After he woke up and saw Moses, Elijah, and Jesus in all of their glory, he was ready to say good-bye to fishing forever and become a full-fledged mountain man. Peter never wanted to leave that mountain—and who could blame him?

But Jesus knew something Peter didn't. Jesus knew He could not remain on that mountain. Jesus knew He must descend from the Mount of Transfiguration so He could ultimately climb Mount Calvary. Although Peter didn't realize it, his desire to begin a building campaign on the Mount of Transfiguration marked the second time he had tried to prevent Christ's suffering.

Prior to the transfiguration when Christ told His disciples He would soon suffer and die, Peter took Jesus aside and gave Him a piece of his mind by saying, "Never, Lord! This shall never happen to You!" The response Jesus gave him must have cut Peter to the quick: "Get behind Me, Satan! You are a stumbling block to Me; you do not have in mind the things of God, but the things of men" (Matthew 16:22–23).

There would be a third time Peter would try to prevent Christ's sufferings. On the night of Jesus' arrest as the soldiers approached Christ, Peter—without wavering—violently pulled a knife and slashed off the ear of one of the soldiers. I love Peter, but it's clear he didn't grasp what Jesus had so diligently tried to teach him.

It wasn't until after the resurrection and ascension that Peter fully understood the necessity of Christ's suffering. Later, when Peter wrote the book of 1 Peter (a book that's only five chapters long) he used the word "suffering" over fifteen times. And two of those references are very noteworthy for us today:

> To the elders among you, I appeal as a fellow elder, a witness of Christ's sufferings and one who also will share in the glory to be revealed.
>
> —1 Peter 5:1

> And the God of all grace, who called you to His eternal glory in Christ, after you have suffered a little while, will Himself restore you and make you strong, firm and steadfast.
>
> —1 Peter 5:10

Finally Peter understood. It was Christ's *suffering* that made it possible for him to share in Christ's *glory*. But there's more. Peter also came to understand that before we can experience eternal glory, we must suffer, too.

My sister, I wonder: Are you suffering today? If so, I hope you'll take comfort from someone who tried—not once, not twice, but three times—to prevent the suffering of Christ. Peter's words, transcribed under the inspiration of the Spirit, were written to remind and encourage you that suffering is the pathway to glory. And you don't want to allow *anything* to prevent you from glorifying God. So, precious sister, even in suffering, *glo.*

<h1>*The Temple:* Glorifying God Through Suffering</h1>

__*Key Principle:*__ *We glorify God in our everyday lives
by responding to persecution and suffering as Christ did.*

I. The _____ of Persecution and Suffering:

    A. For His _____ _____. *John 15:18–21, Phil. 1:29*

    B. For the _____. *2 Tim. 1:8*

    C. For your _____. *1 Pet. 4:12*

    D. For _____. *2 Tim. 3:12*

    E. For _____ _____. *1 Pet. 4:19*

II. The _____ to Persecution and Suffering:

    A. _____ and be _____. *Matt. 5:12, Acts 5:41*

    B. _____ and _____ for your enemies. *Matt. 5:44*

    C. _____ those who _____ you. *Rom. 12:14*

    D. _____ the _____ of Christ. *1 Pet. 2:21–23*

    E. _____ _____ and endure. *1 Pet. 2:19–20*

    F. Do not _____ or be _____. *1 Pet. 3:14*

    G. Do not _____ _____. *1 Pet. 4:12*

    H. Do not _____ _____. *1 Pet. 4:16*

    I. _____ yourself to God and continue to _____ _____. *1 Pet. 4:19*

    J. Be _____, even to the point of _____. *Rev. 2:10*

    Persecution and suffering are the truest tests of _____.

III. The _____ of Persecution and Suffering:

    A. The _____ will be _____. *Acts 1:8, 8:1–4*

    "The blood of the martyrs is the seed of the church." Tertullian

    B. Others will be _____. *Heb. 13:12*

    C. Our _____ will grow _____. *1 Pet. 5:10*

IV. The _____ of Persecution and Suffering:

    A. We'll receive a _____ _____. *Matt. 5:10–12*

    B. We'll be _____ _____ of God's kingdom. *2 Thess. 1:5*

    C. We'll receive the _____ of _____. *Jas. 1:12*

"He is no fool who gives what he cannot keep to gain what he cannot lose." Jim Elliot

The Temple: GOD'S TEMPLE TODAY—YOU!

For a few days this summer, I got away from the big city (Houston) where I live. My friend Myra and I drove several hours west to the Texas Hill Country where she has a lovely place on the Frio River. By day, the view of the Texas Hill Country is truly beautiful—but the nights are spectacular.

As Myra and I sat on her back porch one night, tilting our chins toward the sky, we witnessed something that you just can't see in the big city. Under the canopy of the blackened Hill Country skies, we witnessed Psalm 19:1, "The heavens declare the glory of God; the skies proclaim the work of His hands." It had been a long time since I had seen the great expanse of the heavens so brilliantly lit. I had forgotten just how immense and lush the night skies can be. In fact, just the thought of it right now makes me want to pick up the phone and call Myra to say, "Girl, let's head for the hills!"

Several days ago, I was remembering the glorious view I had seen at Myra's, and a question came to my mind. "I wonder," I thought, "when God tilts His head downward to view the earth and its people, does He clearly see His glory reflected through my life?"

Here in the big city we see only the moon and a very small smattering of stars at night. The glare from manmade lights prevents us from enjoying the panorama of countless numbers of heavenly lights. In my own life, it grieves me to say, I see a parallel truth. At times the glare from my own sin and self prevents God's glory from clearly shining forth through me.

This week we will study the Power Source that God has placed within each one of us that removes the glare of sin and self from our lives and enables us to reflect His light and His glory. That Power Source is the Holy Spirit. As I write this week's lesson, I am asking God to use it to exhort and encourage us to burn more brightly than ever before because of the glorious power of His Spirit within us.

Sister, as God's temple, let's do something together. Let's commit to join the heavens in declaring the glory of God so that when He tilts His head toward us and looks upon this dark, sinful world, He will see far more than just a small smattering of light upon the earth. Let's pray that God will see nothing less than a spectacular, glorious view when He looks our way.

> *May the whole earth be filled with [Your] glory.*
>
> —Psalm 72:19

THIS WEEK'S
KEY PRINCIPLE:

*We glorify
God in our
everyday lives
by allowing
the power of
the Holy Spirit
to flow freely
through us.*

Day One

1. Begin your day of study in prayer and praise to God. Let today's Psalm express the desire of your own heart, and commit to glorify and praise the Lord constantly through your heart and life today.

Pray Today

*O God, we give glory to You all day long
and constantly praise Your name.*
Psalm 44:8 *NLT*

Over the past several weeks, you've seen how God revealed Himself and His glory through the tabernacle, the temple, and through His Son, Jesus. I call this revelation of God "The Story of Glory." It's the story of a gracious, loving God who passionately desires to dwell among men.

After the resurrection and ascension of Christ, God's glory fell once again—but not upon a tabernacle, and not upon a temple. This time God's glory fell upon the lives of ordinary people. Sister, we've come to a very exciting point in our study because this is where you and I really come into "The Story of Glory."

So get ready to glo, girl, because we're about to see how God's glory has come to dwell in us. We're about to learn how we have become *the temple*.

2. Today we'll focus on the commands and promises Christ gave to His followers prior to His ascension into heaven. We'll also discover how these commands and promises were fulfilled. Use the following instructions to complete the chart:

a.   Read Acts 1:1–11, and observe Christ's commands and promises. On the left side of the chart, fill in the blanks (using words from the verses given) to complete the list of Christ's final commands and promises.

b.   Complete the right side of the chart by reading Acts 1:12–14 and Acts 2:1–11, 32. As you read, record how each specific command was obeyed or fulfilled.

Commands and Promises	Commands Obeyed / Promises Fulfilled
Prior to His ascension, Christ commanded His followers not to leave Jerusalem, but to _____ for what the Father had _____ and for what they'd heard of from Him (vv. 4–5).	
Christ promised His followers would be _____ with the _____ _____ (v. 5).	
The Holy Spirit would give Christ's followers _____ (v. 8).	
Christ called them to become His _____ (v. 8).	

3. According to Acts 1:11–13 and Acts 2:1–4, which group of people first received the Holy Spirit?

    Gentiles   Samaritans   Jews/Israelites

4. Read Acts 8:5–17, and answer the following questions:

    a.   Where did Philip preach about Christ?

    b.   How did Philip obey the final commands of Christ?

    c.   How did Philip witness the fulfillment of Christ's promises?

    d.   Which group of people received the Holy Spirit in this passage? Please circle your answer:

        Gentiles   Samaritans   Israelites

5. Read Acts 10:1–5, 34–48, and answer the following questions:

    a.   Where did Peter proclaim Christ?

    b.   How did Peter obey the final commands of Christ?

    c.   How did Peter witness the fulfillment of Christ's promises?

    d.   Which group of people received the Holy Spirit in this passage? Please circle your answer:

        Gentiles   Samaritans   Israelites

e. How did Peter's companions respond to the outpouring of the Holy Spirit upon this group of people, and what did God confirm to them through this experience (vv. 45 and 47)?

6. How do the final commands of Christ apply to you?

_____

_____

_____

_____

_____

_____

_____

_____

_____

— *Day Two* —

1. Your life is a book others are reading. Spend a few moments in prayer, and ask God to be glorified through every chapter of the story of your life. Ask Him to give you opportunities today to share with others the amazing things He has done in your life.

Publish His glorious deeds among the nations.
Tell everyone about the amazing things He does.
Psalm 96:3 *NLT*

Today you will witness the power of the Holy Spirit in the life of Stephen, the first martyr of the Christian faith. The glory of God was obvious in Stephen's life—and in his death.

As you study Stephen's life, you will see many parallels between Stephen and Christ. And as you read Stephen's sermon in Acts 7, you will observe many parallels with our own study of *The Temple*. May the life and death of Stephen exhort and inspire us to glorify God, no matter the cost.

2. Read Acts 6, and describe Stephen's character.

3. Review Acts 6, and record the similarities between Stephen and Christ. Be sure to note their common source of power.

4. Before he was martyred, Stephen preached one of the most stirring sermons ever recorded. You are about to read that sermon. Yes, it is lengthy, but nowhere else in Scripture is the story of God's glory more succinctly told. Engage all of your senses as you read by: (a) passionately reading it aloud, or by (b) reading it silently and imagining yourself among the crowd who heard it that day. Now please read Acts 7, then record how Stephen's sermon affected you.

5. What did Stephen see before he died (vv. 54–55)? (Don't you think it's beautiful that Stephen received a standing ovation from Jesus before he died? Glory!)

6. Please read Acts 8:1–4 and Acts 11:19–21. How was God increasingly glorified through Stephen's death?

7. In Acts 7:58, you saw the first mention in Scripture of Saul, who later became the apostle Paul. Please read the following scriptures, briefly noting what you learn about Saul.

   a. Acts 7:58–8:3

   b. Acts 9:1–29

8. As you review Acts 9:17–29, how did Saul's life and ministry parallel Stephen's life and ministry? What did they have in common?

My sister, I realize you have studied long today, but please take just a few minutes more to read something the Apostle Paul wrote many years after his conversion. I believe it will bless you tremendously.

9. While Paul was imprisoned in Rome (he was arrested for proclaiming the gospel), he wrote the book of Philippians. Please read Philippians 1:19–24, and think about how Stephen may have influenced Paul's attitude about life and death.

10. How has the Holy Spirit spoken to you through your study of Stephen and Paul today?

_____

_____

_____

_____

_____

_____

_____

Day Three

1. Before you begin your study today, prayerfully ask God to let the ones you love most see His glory visibly shining in *your* life.

   Let us see Your miracles again;
   let our children see Your glory at work.
   Psalm 90:16 *NLT*

   Your study today will focus on the baptism and work of the Holy Spirit. Without the Holy Spirit we would be spiritually impotent. You may think the word "impotent" is an improper term to use, yet I can think of none better. After you have done your study today, I think you will totally agree with me.

   The only way we can reproduce and bear spiritual fruit in our lives is through the power of the Holy Spirit. Don't be an impotent Christian. Be *potent*. It really is possible, thanks to the awesome power of the Holy Spirit.

2. Begin by writing our key passage for this study, 1 Corinthians 6:19–20, in the space below. Do your best to record it from memory, but if you need a little help, use your Bible.

3. According to 1 Corinthians 6:19–20, please describe how you became the temple of the Holy Spirit.

4. Before you became a Christian, what work was the Holy Spirit doing in your life? To answer this question, please read John 16:7–11 and John 6:44.

5. To more fully understand the work of the Holy Spirit in salvation, please read a beautiful passage in Titus 3:3–5, and answer the following questions:

   a. Before salvation, what were we like (v. 3)?

   b. How were we saved and changed (v. 4–5)?

   c. How did we receive the Holy Spirit (v. 6)?

After reading that passage from Titus, don't you just want to shout, "Glory to God!" Go ahead. Give God a good glory shout right now in praise and thanks to Him for His mercy, kindness, love and for the outpouring of His Spirit upon your life.

6. For the remainder of your study today, you will be studying the after effects of salvation—the ongoing work of the Holy Spirit in the life of every believer. Please read each scripture reference on the following chart, and briefly summarize what you learn about the work of the Holy Spirit in our lives. And if you need to stop and shout, "Glory," another time or two, go right ahead!

The Glorious Work of the Holy Spirit

John 14:26
Acts 16:6–7

Romans 8:26–27

1 Corinthians 2:12–16

2 Corinthians 3:17–18

7. As you reflect upon your study today, how can you know the Holy Spirit is at work in your life? What specific evidence do you see of His work in your life *today?*

_____

_____

_____

_____

_____

_____

_____

_____

_____

_____

_____

Insights

— ❧ *Day Four* ❧ —

1. Are you trusting the Lord today in the trials and struggles you're facing? If so, by faith claim the promise contained within today's Psalm, and prayerfully commit to glorify Him, even as you wait for Him to rescue you.

> *Trust Me in your times of trouble,*
> *and I will rescue you, and you will give Me glory.*
> Psalm 50:15 *NLT*

Pray Today

The Temple

Yesterday we learned about the work of the Spirit before salvation, at salvation, and after salvation. Today we will continue in our study of the Holy Spirit focusing on His ongoing work in our lives.

When we allow the Spirit to lead and control us, our lives will produce the character and attributes of God. And when we exhibit the character and attributes of God, we glorify God. Are you glo-ing right now? Perhaps you're not quite sure. By the end of today's lesson, you're gonna know if you glo.

2. Read the following scriptures, and underline the repeated words and phrases:

> *Remain in Me, and I will remain in you. No branch can bear fruit by itself; it must remain in the vine. Neither can you bear fruit unless you remain in Me. I am the vine; you are the branches. If a man remains in Me and I in him, he will bear much fruit; apart from Me you can do nothing.*
>
> —John 15:4–5

> *This is to My Father's glory, that you bear much fruit, showing yourselves to be My disciples.*
>
> —John 15:8

3. Answer the following questions regarding the verses you just read from John 15:

   a. According to John 15:8, how is God glorified, and what does spiritual fruit prove?

   b. How does Jesus describe us in John 15:4–5? Please answer this very simply.

   c. How does Jesus describe Himself in John 15:4–5? Again, keep your answer very simple.

   d. Is it possible to produce spiritual fruit in our lives apart from Christ? Please circle your answer: Yes   No

   e. Have you ever *tried* to produce spiritual fruit in your life apart from the power of Christ? Please circle your answer: Yes   No

   f. If you answered "yes" to the previous question, briefly describe the result of your efforts.

   g. According to these verses, how is spiritual fruit produced in our lives?

4. What exactly is "spiritual fruit"? Please read Galatians 5:22–23, and record a list of the fruit of the Spirit.

In order to glorify God in our everyday lives, we must reflect His attributes and His character. His attributes include, of course, the same characteristics as the fruit of the Spirit with one exception: self-control. Because God is God, He has absolute authority to do as He righteously wills. We, His children, must exercise self-control, but He is sovereign and in complete control.

5. Please read each of the following verses. These verses parallel God's attributes with the fruit of the Spirit. You do not need to record anything (unless you so desire). After you've read each passage, stop for a moment to:

    •   Prayerfully praise and thank God for the specific attribute about Him that is taught in that passage.

    •   Confess to God the specific ways you've been challenged (or have failed) to consistently reflect that attribute through your life.

    •   Express to God your desire to abide in Him and to allow His Spirit to flow through your life.

    •   Ask God to produce that same fruit, that specific characteristic, in your life today.

    a. **Love**—Romans 8:38–39

    b. **Joy**—Nehemiah 8:10 (You may need to use the table of contents in the front of your Bible to find Nehemiah—it's a little hard to locate.)

    c. **Peace**—2 Thessalonians 3:16

    d. **Patience (Longsuffering** in the KJV) and **Kindness**—Psalm 103:8–14

    e. **Goodness**—Psalm 25:8

    f. **Faithfulness**—2 Timothy 2:13

    g. **Gentleness (Meekness** in the KJV)—Isaiah 40:11

In Charles Stanley's excellent book *The Wonderful Spirit-Filled Life*, he says:

> Jesus makes a clear delineation between the vine and the branch. The two are not the same. *He* is the vine; *we* are the branches. The two are joined but not one. The common denominator in nature is the sap. The sap is the life of the vine and its branches. Cut off the flow of sap to the branch, and it slowly withers and dies. As the branch draws its life from the vine, so we draw life from Christ. *To abide in Christ is to draw upon His life.* His life is made available through the presence of the Holy Spirit in our lives. The abiding presence of the Holy Spirit is the life of Christ in us.[1]

Isn't that good? You may want to pick up a copy of Dr. Stanley's book—it's *all* good! And isn't it glorious to know we don't have to *do* anything to produce spiritual fruit. We must simply *abide in Christ*, and the fruit will flow—and we will glo!

6. How has God demonstrated His attributes to you recently? Take some time to think about this, and journal your insights as the Holy Spirit leads you.

_____

_____

_____

_____

_____

_____

_____

_____

_____

_____

Day Five

1. Because God has sealed us with His Spirit, and because we are His temple, we can never be separated from Him. He is dwelling within us. Why not spend some time on your knees before the Lord in prayer. Thank Him today for the indwelling, ongoing work of the Holy Spirit in your life.

> *Where can I go from Your Spirit?*
> *Where can I flee from Your presence?*
> Psalm 139:7

In our final day of study this week, we will briefly overview the gifts of the Spirit. At salvation, the Holy Spirit came to live within you—and when He arrived, He brought gifts! These gifts will fit you perfectly, and you will

enjoy them immensely. Trust me, you're not going to want to exchange or return your spiritual gifts like other gifts you have received. And when you use your spiritual gifts, you will become a gift yourself as God uses you to edify and strengthen others. Spiritual gifts—today's topic—the gifts that really do keep on giving!

2. Please read 1 Corinthians 12:4–31, and record your answers to the following:

    a.   What do you think Paul means in verses 4–6?

    b.   According to verse 7, who receives spiritual gifts, and what is the purpose of spiritual gifts?

    c.   Please list the spiritual gifts (vv. 8–10, 28).

    d.   According to verse 11, are we allowed to choose the gift(s) we want. Please explain your answer.

    e.   Summarize in one sentence the primary point Paul is making in verses 12–27.

    f.   Summarize in one sentence the primary point Paul is making in verses 29–31.

3. Please read Ephesians 4:7–8, 11–16, and answer the following questions:

    a.   According to verse 12, what is the purpose of spiritual gifts?

    b.   According to verses 14–16, what is the result of spiritual gifts when they are exercised within the church?

The Temple

4. Please read 1 Peter 4:10–11, and answer the following questions:

    a. According to verse 10, how are we instructed to use our spiritual gifts?

    b. According to verse 11, what is the purpose of spiritual gifts?

    How can you know what your spiritual gift(s) is? Many Christians discover their gift(s) as they serve within various areas of their churches. And sometimes they find out through trial and error (I know this from personal experience).

    If you're unsure about which spiritual gift(s) you have received, don't be discouraged. Count on it, God *has* given you one or more spiritual gifts (1 Corinthians 12:7), and He *will* faithfully reveal your gift(s) to you as you continue to seek and serve Him. In fact, He may use other Christians to help you identify your spiritual gift(s).

    Whether you can identify your spiritual gift(s) or not, God has called all of us to serve Him through the body of Christ, the church. So how can you serve Him if you're unsure of your spiritual gift(s)? Great question! You're about to discover the answer for yourself.

5. Whether we know our spiritual gift(s) or not, the final verse in 1 Corinthians 12 points us to the highest way to serve God and others. Please read 1 Corinthians 12:31–13:13, and briefly summarize how to serve God with excellence even when we're unsure about our spiritual gift(s).

6. What have you learned this week as you have studied the Holy Spirit? How is the Lord leading you to follow Him as a result of the time you have spent with Him in prayer and in His Word? Please reflect back over this past week, and use your journal page to pour out your thoughts on paper.

My Journal

THIS WEEK THE LORD...

_____

_____

_____

_____

_____

_____

_____

_____

AS A RESULT, I...

_____

_____

_____

_____

_____

_____

_____

_____

_____

Go with the flow. Now there's a little piece of advice I've heard dozens of times. Usually it just means to do whatever *I* think is best. Or sometimes it means to do what everyone *else* thinks is best. And it may even mean that I shouldn't even think about it at all—just let go and *go* with it whatever *it* may be.

Here's a much better saying: Glo with the flow. Translation: Glorify God by allowing the Holy Spirit to flow in your life. Going with the flow can get me in a big mess fast! But when I glo with the flow, God's Spirit steers me away from messes—He can even get me out of messes that *I've* made.

So here are my parting words of exhortation to you, my sister: Let the Spirit flow, and He'll let your life *glo!*

The Temple: GLO-ING WITH THE FLOW PART I

Key Principle: *We glorify God in our everyday lives by allowing the power of His Spirit to flow freely through us.*

Or do you not know that your body is a temple of the Holy Spirit who is in you, whom you have from God, and that you are not your own? For you have been bought with a price: therefore glorify God in your body.

—1 Corinthians 6:19–20 *NASB*

I. _____ of the Spirit

   1. *Ezekiel 36:26–27:* God promises to put _____ _____ in His people.
   2. *John 4:7–15:* Jesus promises to give _____ _____ to those who ask.
   3. *John 7:37–39:* Jesus identifies the _____ _____ as His _____.
   4. *John 14:16–18:* Jesus promises that the Spirit will be _____ us and _____ us _____.

   This means: The Holy Spirit is promised to _____ _____.

II. _____of the Spirit

   1. *John 14:16–18:* He is a _____; He is a "_____."
   2. *Acts 5:3–4, 2 Cor. 3:17–18:* He is _____; He is _____.
   3. *1 Cor. 2:11, 12:11:* He possesses _____ _____.
   4. *Gen. 1:2, Titus 3:3–5:* He produces _____ _____.

   This means: _____ _____ is in us through the Holy Spirit!

III. _____ _____ with the Spirit

   1. *John 14:16:* Our _____/
      _____.
   2. *John 14:26:* Our _____.
   3. *John 16:8:* Our _____.
   4. *John 16:13:* Our _____.

   5. *John 16:13–15:* He _____ to us.
   6. *Acts 16:6–7:* He _____ us.
   7. *Romans 8:26–27:* He _____ for us.
   8. *Eph. 4:30:* We can _____ Him.

   This means: We have an ongoing, _____ _____ with the Holy Spirit!

IV. _____of the Holy Spirit

   1. *Acts 1:8:* Power for _____.
   2. *Romans 8:9–13:* Power over _____.

   3. *1 Cor. 12:7,11:* Spiritual _____.
   4. *Gal. 5:22–23:* Spiritual _____.

   This means: We will see the _____/_____ of His Spirit in our lives, and _____ _____, too.

But, how can we practically experience the power of His Spirit in our everyday lives?

V. _____ _____ for Life in the Spirit

   1. *John 15:5:* We must recognize and admit: _____ from Him, I can do _____.
   2. *John 15:4, Gal. 5:16:* We must choose to _____ in Christ and to _____ in His Spirit.
   3. The difference between abiding and walking is:
      * abiding is to _____, to _____ in close, intimate fellowship with Christ.
      * walking is to practically live out, to _____ _____ _____ with Christ.
   4. The similarity between abiding and walking is:
      * they both are possible through the _____, _____ Holy Spirit.
      * they both are our _____, our _____.
        The glorious results: * _____ _____,
                * lives that _____ _____.

The Temple: GLORIFYING GOD IN THE SPIRIT

As I was writing this study, I received a letter from Jeanette Willis, a dear friend of mine, letting me know she was praying for me. In her letter, Jeanette also said she "felt moved to share a small page from (her) life" with me. I, in turn, feel moved to share Jeanette's letter—with her blessing—with you this week:

> As a young person growing up in the church, I was always taught that my purpose in life was to glorify God. That was the textbook answer to why I was here. Then, as an adult, I struggled because I didn't really have a handle on what it meant to glorify God.
>
> I thought about women I knew who were always charming and gracious…is that what it meant (to glorify God)? I thought of people who always seemed to be happy. Then as the "praise the Lord" movement came about, I supposed glorifying God meant saying that all the time, or playing Christian music all day. Whatever I imagined it to be, it did not fit me…a stay-at-home mom, with one income, not having a second car for the first seven years of (my oldest child's) life, having a baby at age 35, having a husband who traveled a lot, coming to the end of the day exhausted and sweating in humid Houston!!!
>
> As the kids got older, I still didn't understand how to glorify (God) in **everything**. I worked at a church and taught Sunday school, but that was not **everything**. Many times it seemed like even that was not very glorifying!
>
> Then one day, while I was listening to Christian radio, Tony Evans gave me the simplest, clearest explanation. He said that glorifying God simply means to make God look good in everything I do or say. Thank you, Tony! I can't tell you what a relief and rejoicing that was for me to learn. That was something I could understand. I can make God look good by doing the wash well, by being considerate of others, by fixing a nice meal, and in all of the daily routine tasks. I don't have to be "super spiritual," I just need to do the job well. I have learned that I can bless others anywhere that I go. It is just that simple.
>
> Laurie, I don't know if you can use this in any way or not. It is just what has worked for me. In fact, I use this with my family in whatever they have to do, by encouraging them to remember to make God look good. Even the grandkids can understand that.

Thank you, Tony, and thank you, Jeanette! What a practical and encouraging word her letter is to us. As we choose to make God look good through our words, deeds, and attitudes, we will glorify God in our everyday lives.

THIS WEEK'S KEY PRINCIPLE:

We glorify God in our everyday lives by choosing to be controlled by the Spirit.

With all my heart, I want to make God look good in every word I say, in everything I do, and in every thought I think—and I believe that is your heart's desire as well, or you probably wouldn't have persevered to this ninth week of study! But unfortunately, there is a constant conflict we experience as we seek to make God look good. It's the conflict between our spirit and our flesh.

This week we'll be studying the war we wage every day: the war against our old, sinful nature. But be encouraged. We can win this war one battle at a time through the indwelling power of the Holy Spirit. Victory is ours for the taking. So let's get aggressive and declare war on *anything* that prevents us from making God look good. And come to think of it, we already have a battle cry: *Let's GLO, girl!*

— ✨ *Day One* ✨ —

1. By now I'm sure you're aware of the goal of this study: to learn how to become a woman who glorifies God. By faith, I trust that goal is becoming an ever-growing reality in your life. Spend some time with the Lord in prayer, and commit to put Psalm 71:8 at the very top of your "to do" list today—and every day.

I declare Your glory all day long.
Psalm 71:8 *NLT*

For most of the week, our study will center on the book of Romans. You'll find lots of good news in Romans as the apostle Paul explains the glorious results of your salvation and the ongoing work of the Holy Spirit in your life. But before we dig into Romans, let's review and analyze our key passage for this study:

Or do you not know that your body is a temple of the Holy Spirit who is in you whom you have from God, and that you are not your own? For you have been bought with a price: therefore glorify God in your body.

—1 Corinthians 6:19–20 *NASB*

2. Please read 1 Corinthians 6:19–20, and answer the following questions by checking the appropriate box.

   a. ☐ yes ☐ no Is it a *fact* that you are a temple of the Holy Spirit?

   b. ☐ yes ☐ no Is it a *fact* that you have received the Holy Spirit from God?

   c. ☐ yes ☐ no Is it a *fact* that you are not your own?

   d. ☐ yes ☐ no Is it a *fact* that you have been purchased by God?

   e. ☐ yes ☐ no Is it a *fact* that you now have the supernatural ability to glorify God through your life?

3. Keeping in mind the facts you've just identified from 1 Corinthians 6:19–20, please read the following passage from Romans:

> *I don't understand myself at all, for I really want to do what is right, but I don't do it. Instead, I do the very thing I hate. … When I want to do good, I don't. And when I try not to do wrong, I do it anyway. …It seems to be a fact of life that when I want to do what is right, I inevitably do what is wrong. I love God's law with all my heart. But there is another law at work within me that is at war with my mind…*
>
> —Romans 7:15–23 *NLT*

4. Before we can fully appreciate the truths of our study this week, we need to reflect on what we've just read from Romans 7. So let's take a few moments to honestly and transparently answer the following questions:

   a.   Do you identify or relate to what Paul wrote in Romans 7:15–23?

   ❏ yes   ❏ no

   b.   If you answered "yes" to the previous question, please share two examples in which you are currently struggling to do right and often find yourself doing wrong.

   c.   Although you may still struggle with sin, are you also experiencing the transformational power of the indwelling Holy Spirit in your life? In other words, are you experiencing the ability to overcome sinful patterns in your life?

   ❏ yes   ❏ no   ❏ unsure

   Thank you, dear sister, for your honesty and openness. Now let me be honest with you. I struggle with sin, too—*every day*. That's why Lamentations 3:21–23 is one of my favorite passages: "This I recall to mind, therefore I have hope. The Lord's lovingkindnesses indeed never cease, for His compassions never fail. They are new every morning; great is Thy faithfulness" (*NASB*). What hope and encouragement I find in those words!

   Now let's talk about the passage you just read from Romans 7:15–23. I believe these verses express the problem all Christians (even Paul) experience. And personally, I thank God for Paul's honesty in sharing his struggle with us. But even more than that, I thank God Romans 7:15–23 is surrounded by some victorious truths in the chapters that precede and follow it So for now, let's back away from Romans 7 and move into Romans 6 where we'll find some hope-filled facts that apply to every believer in Christ.

5. Please carefully read the following passage, Romans 6:1–8, from the New Living Translation:

> **NOTE: In Romans 5, Paul has been contrasting the law (the Old Covenant) and grace (the New Covenant). In Romans 5:20, Paul said,** *"as people sinned more and more, God's wonderful kindness became more abundant"* **(NLT). Anticipating that his readers might misunderstand and think he is teaching them to sin more so that they may experience more of God's grace, Paul begins Romans 6 with a question and a very clear answer to clarify himself:** *"should we keep on sinning so that God can show us more and more kindness and forgiveness? Of course not!"* **(6:1–2, NLT).**

Romans 6:1–8 *(NLT)*

¹Well then, should we keep on sinning so that God can show us more and more kindness and forgiveness?

²Of course not! Since we have died to sin, how can we continue to live in it?

³Or have you forgotten that when we became Christians and were baptized to become one with Christ Jesus, we died with Him?

⁴For we died and were buried with Christ by baptism. And just as Christ was raised from the dead by the glorious power of the Father, now we also may live new lives.

⁵Since we have been united with Him in His death, we will also be raised as He was.

⁶Our old sinful selves were crucified with Christ so that sin might lose its power in our lives. We are no longer slaves to sin.

⁷For when we died with Christ we were set free from the power of sin.

⁸And since we died with Christ, we know we will also share His new life.

6. Using the passage you just read from Romans 6, please answer the following questions:

a. What *fact* is stated in verse 2?

b. What question is asked in verse 2?

c. Briefly summarize the answer to this question from verses 3–4.

d. Paul refers to "we" in this passage several times. According to verse 3, to whom is Paul referring when he says "we?"

e.   According to verse 4, what kind of lives are "we" to live?

f.   What *fact* is stated in verse 6?

g.   What are the results of this *fact* (v. 6)?

h.   What *fact* is stated in verse 8?

The passage from Romans 6 clearly teaches that salvation produces a new life, a changed life, and a life that has power over sin. Within these verses, we learn that true salvation results in *immediate* change, *progressive* change, and *future* change.

You see, at salvation, we were freed from the **penalty** of sin, which is death and separation from God. This is called **justification**. At salvation, we were also freed from the **power** of sin through the baptism/indwelling of the Holy Spirit so that we are no longer slaves of sin. This is called **sanctification**. In the future (when our mortal bodies die and we are with Christ in heaven), we will be freed from the very **presence** of sin, and we will receive eternal life with Christ and new bodies that cannot sin. This is called **glorification**.

Therefore, as a Christian, you *are* justified, you *are being* sanctified, and you *will be* glorified. Justification is a past, completed act in the life of the Christian. Sanctification is an ongoing work within the life of the Christian. Glorification is the future reality for all Christians.

But please know this: the evidence of true salvation is a *changed* life not a *perfect* life—as Paul taught in the passage you read earlier from Romans 7. 1 John 1:8 says, "If we say we have no sin, we are deceiving ourselves, and the truth is not in us" (*NASB*). As Christians, we *will* sin, **but** we will *not* be slaves to sin as we were before salvation. In fact, 1 John 3:7–9 says, "let no one deceive you; the one who practices righteousness is righteous, just as He is righteous; the one who practices sin is of the devil… No one who is born of God practices sin" (*NASB*). In 1 John, practicing sin means slavery to sin. Practicing sin denotes a lifestyle of habitual sin, and this does *not* characterize the life of a true Christian. On the contrary, righteousness should characterize the life of the Christian.

I love the way my pastor, Dr. John Morgan, says it, "Being a Christian doesn't mean that you'll never sin again. It just means that you've *enjoyed* your last sin." So true! As Christians, sin brings conviction and breaks our fellowship (not our relationship) with God. Yes we'll sin, but we'll be *miserable* when we do. Been there—many times. Again, thank God for Lamentations 3:21–23.

7. As we close our time of study today, please go back and review your answer to Question 4c, then answer the following questions as they apply to you:

    a. If you answered "yes," please take a few moments to record a brief note or praise to God for the specific ways you have experienced His transformational power at work in your life.

    b. If you're unsure about whether or not you've ever experienced the transformational power of the Holy Spirit in your life, please take a few moments to examine your life by simply dropping to your knees before God in prayer. Ask Him to reveal to you whether you have ever truly been saved. Ask Him to show you whether your heart has ever been changed. If you have no assurance of your salvation, and if you've seen no evidence of the power of His Spirit in your life, please take time to read the article in the back of this workbook entitled, *A Change of Heart*. Perhaps the Lord is drawing you to salvation today.

    c. If you answered "no," and you have never experienced the life-changing, transformational power of the Holy Spirit in your life, dear one, you can. If the Lord is convicting you today and drawing you unto Himself, please respond *now*. Turn to the article in the back of this workbook entitled *A Change of Heart*, and give your heart to God today by acknowledging your sin, by placing your faith in Christ, and by receiving His gift of salvation. You can experience His indwelling power, His love, His joy, and His peace today.

8. How has the Lord spoken to you today? How will you respond to the *facts* you've studied from 1 Corinthians 6:19–20 and Romans 6:1–8?

_____

_____

_____

_____

_____

_____

_____

_____

Day Two

1. God wants you to share what He's done in your life with others. As you share—as you brag on God—you're giving Him glory. Whether or not you have children, God is calling you to share His glory with the next generation, so their faith will be strengthened and encouraged. As you begin your study today in prayer, ask God to show you someone who needs to hear about the glorious deeds He has done in your life—then tell them.

> *We will not hide these truths from our children*
> *but will tell the next generation about the glorious*
> *deeds of the Lord. We will tell of His power and the*
> *mighty miracles He did.*
> Psalm 78:4 *NLT*

Today you will continue to study from the apostle Paul's magnificent treatise, the book of Romans. Paul was a master theologian, a brilliant scholar, and a true hero of the faith. But he was also very human. His "humanness" is expressed all throughout his inspired writings, and I'm so glad. As I read about Paul's struggles, I can identify with him, and I am greatly encouraged.

Perhaps Paul's most transparent words are found in Romans 7. These will be the focus of today's study. In Romans 7, you'll read about Paul's problem, my problem, and your problem. And today we're going to get to the root of the problem. I don't like problems, but I've learned that if I ignore them, they usually don't go away—in fact, they usually just get bigger.

Sister, we've got a big problem, and today we're going to face up to it. Why? Because it's The Primary Problem we face as we seek to glorify God in our everyday lives. Girl, let's face this problem head-on, like a man—a man like Paul.

2. Please begin your study today by reviewing the following:

    a. The facts of 1 Corinthians 6:19–20 from Question 2 in yesterday's assignment.

    b. The context of 1 Corinthians 6:19–20 by reading 1 Corinthians 6:9–20. Then please record why Paul reminded the Corinthians that they were temples of the Holy Spirit.

3. Please read the following scriptures and briefly summarize what you learn from them:

   a.   Galatians 5:17

   b.   1 Peter 2:11

4. According to the scriptures you just studied, what ongoing war do all Christians face?

5. Carefully read the following passage from Romans 7 from the New Living Translation. As you read, please seek to identify the root of Paul's problem—and ours.

Romans 7:15–25 (NLT)

15 I don't understand myself at all, for I really want to do what is right, but I don't do it. Instead, I do the very thing I hate.

16 I know perfectly well that what I am doing is wrong, and my bad conscience shows that I agree that the law is good.

17 But I can't help myself, because it is sin inside me that makes me do these evil things.

18 I know I am rotten through and through so far as my old sinful nature is concerned. No matter which way I turn, I can't make myself do right. I want to, but I can't.

19 When I want to do good, I don't. And when I try not to do wrong, I do it anyway.

20 But if I am doing what I don't want to do, I am not really the one doing it; the sin within me is doing it.

21 It seems to be a fact of life that when I want to do what is right, I inevitably do what is wrong.

22 I love God's law with all my heart.

23 But there is another law at work within me that is at war with my mind. This law wins the fight and makes me a slave to the sin that is still within me.

24 Oh, what a miserable person I am! Who will free me from this life that is dominated by sin?

25 Thank God! The answer is in Jesus Christ our Lord. So you see how it is: In my mind I really want to obey God's law, but because of my sinful nature I am a slave to sin.

6. Please answer the following questions:

    a. What problem is Paul experiencing?

    b. What is the root of Paul's problem?

    c. What two forces are at war with one another in Paul's life?

    d. What is the solution to Paul's problem?

      In Romans 7:18 and 25, Paul refers to the sinful nature. The King James Version and the New American Standard translation use the word "flesh" in these same verses. The sinful nature, or the flesh, is the root problem of the ongoing war we experience in our Christian walk.

      Does this mean that our physical flesh is our problem and our enemy? No, *The Bible Knowledge Commentary* says that the sinful nature, or flesh, does not refer to "literal physical or material flesh, but (to) the principle of sin that expresses itself through one's mind and body."[1]

      The Greek word for sinful nature, or flesh, is "sarx" which means "sinfulness, proneness to sin, the carnal nature, the seat of carnal appetites and desires, of sinful passions and affections whether physical or moral."[2]

      At salvation we receive a new nature through the indwelling of the Holy Spirit. The old sinful nature, however, is not eradicated at salvation. Therefore, these two natures are at war within the life of every believer. The old nature, which produces the desire to walk in sinfulness, is at war with the new nature, which produces the desire to walk in righteousness (Romans 8:5).

7. As you continue to look at the root problem we face (the sinful nature), please read Romans 8:1–16 on the next page from the New Living Translation. Carefully observe what you learn about the sinful nature.

Romans 8:1–16 _(NLT)_

[1]So now there is no condemnation for those who belong to Christ Jesus.

[2]For the power of the life-giving Spirit has freed you through Christ Jesus from the power of sin that leads to death.

[3]The law of Moses could not save us, because of our sinful nature. But God put into effect a different plan to save us. He sent His own Son in a human body like ours, except that ours are sinful. God destroyed sin's control over us by giving His Son as a sacrifice for our sins.

[4]He did this so that the requirement of the law would be fully accomplished for us who no longer follow our sinful nature but instead follow the Spirit.

[5]Those who are dominated by the sinful nature think about sinful things, but those who are controlled by the Holy Spirit think about things that please the Spirit.

[6]If your sinful nature controls your mind, there is death. But if the Holy Spirit controls your mind, there is life and peace.

[7]For the sinful nature is always hostile to God. It never did obey God's laws, and it never will.

[8]That's why those who are still under the control of their sinful nature can never please God.

[9]But you are not controlled by your sinful nature. You are controlled by the Spirit if you have the Spirit of God living in you. (And remember that those who do not have the Spirit of Christ living in them are not Christians at all.)

[10]Since Christ lives within you, even though your body will die because of sin, your spirit is alive because you have been made right with God.

[11]The Spirit of God, who raised Jesus from the dead, lives in you. And just as He raised Christ from the dead, He will give life to your mortal body by this same Spirit living within you.

[12]So, dear brothers and sisters, you have no obligation whatsoever to do what your sinful nature urges you to do.

[13]For if you keep on following it, you will perish. But if through the power of the Holy Spirit you turn from it and its evil deeds, you will live.

[14]For all who are led by the Spirit of God are children of God.

[15]So you should not be like cowering, fearful slaves. You should behave instead like God's very own children, adopted into His family— calling Him "Father, dear Father."

[16]For His Holy Spirit speaks to us deep in our hearts and tells us that we are God's children.

8. Using the Romans 7 and 8 passages from the New Living Translation, please read only the scriptures listed on the following chart. As you read, briefly summarize what you learn about the sinful nature:

The Sinful Nature/The Flesh

Romans 7:18
Romans 7:25
Romans 8:3
Romans 8:4
Romans 8:5
Romans 8:6
Romans 8:7
Romans 8:8
Romans 8:9
Romans 8:12
Romans 8:13

9. Well, you've identified the problem we face as we seek to glorify God in our bodies. What did you learn about the sinful nature today that you can apply to your life right now?

_____

_____

_____

_____

_____

_____

_____

_____

— *Day Three* —

1. The fullness of God's glory is beyond our comprehension. But please meditate for a few moments upon the attributes He's revealed to you. Then spend some time in prayer just praising Him—even though mere words can't begin to express His glory half enough.

Who can list the glorious miracles of the Lord?
Who can ever praise Him half enough.
Psalm 106:2 *NLT*

   Yesterday you studied the root problem we face as we seek to glorify God: our sinful nature that wars against our new nature in Christ.

   Today we'll focus on the *solution* to our problem. Is it possible to experience victory over our sinful nature? Hallelujah, yes, it is! How? By applying the truths of God's Word to our lives. It's not enough to just know the facts about God's Word. If we want to experience empowered, victorious lives, we must *apply* the Truth to our everyday lives.

   Do you really want to *glo* for God? Then take the truths you study today and *use* them, *live* them, *apply* them to your life, and you really will *glo, girl.*

2. Please read the following passage, Romans 6:11–19, from the New Living Translation, observing carefully the commands and instructions within these verses.

<u>**Romans 6:11–19** *(NLT)*</u>

[11]So you should consider yourselves dead to sin and able to live for the glory of God through Christ Jesus.

[12]Do not let sin control the way you live; do not give in to its lustful desires.

[13]Do not let any part of your body become a tool of wickedness, to be used for sinning. Instead, give yourselves completely to God since you have been given new life. And use your whole body as a tool to do what is right for the glory of God.

[14]Sin is no longer your master, for you are no longer subject to the law, which enslaves you to sin. Instead, you are free by God's grace.

[15]So since God's grace has set us free from the law, does this mean we can go on sinning? Of course not!

[16]Don't you realize that whatever you choose to obey becomes your master? You can choose sin, which leads to death, or you can choose to obey God and receive His approval.

[17]Thank God! Once you were slaves of sin, but now you have obeyed with all your heart the new teaching God has given you.

[18]Now you are free from sin, your old master, and you have become slaves to your new master, righteousness.

[19]I speak this way, using the illustration of slaves and masters, because it is easy to understand. Before, you let yourselves be slaves of impurity and lawlessness. Now, you must choose to be slaves of righteousness so that you will become holy.

3. The solution to the conflict between our sinful nature and our new nature is found within the commands and instructions of Romans 6:11–19 and 8:1–16. In this assignment, you'll be compiling these commands and instructions on the following chart. Please look up each verse listed on the chart, then record the command or instruction given in that verse regarding how to experience victory over the flesh. Use the New Living Translation passages from today's study and from your Day Two homework as you refer to each verse on the chart.

How To Experience Victory Over The Sinful Nature/The Flesh

Romans 6:11
Romans 6:12
Romans 6:13

Romans 6:19
Romans 8:12–13

The chart you just completed gives us the instructions we need to win the daily battles we face with our sinful nature. Most of these instructions are very clear. They involve making daily choices to stand against sin and surrender to the Spirit.

But the first command in Romans 6:11 is a little difficult to understand. Romans 6:11 instructs us to "count (our)selves as dead to sin but alive to God in Christ Jesus" (*NLT*). What does this mean? *The Bible Knowledge Commentary* says this scripture teaches that we are to "recognize that fact (the fact that we have died to sin) and not continue in sin."[3] This is "an attitude of (the) mind that a believer has died to sin."[4]

So before we do anything in the daily warfare we face, we must first mentally "count (our)selves as dead to sin but alive to God in Christ Jesus" (*NLT*). In other words, we've got to believe these three facts:

Fact 1: At salvation, we were freed from the penalty of sin.

Fact 2: At salvation, we were also freed from sin's power.

Fact 3: At salvation, we were empowered to new life through the Holy Spirit.

Those are the facts, but knowing them is not enough. Every day we must embrace and believe them as we stand firm in the war against our sinful nature.

4. According to Romans 6:12–13 and 19, my fellow female warrior, what do you have the power to do, and why are you to do it?

5. According to Romans 8:12–13, my courageous sister in Christ, what do you have the power to do and how?

6. There is one final passage I'd like for you to study today. Please read Titus 2:11–14, then answer the following questions:

a.   As Christians, what are we instructed to do (vv. 12–13)?

b.   As Christians, what should motivate us to live godly lives (v. 13)?

c.   What did Christ redeem us from, and what is the result of our redemption (v. 14)?

    My sister, you now have the instructions to enable you to overcome your flesh and glorify God in your everyday life. I encourage you to use them daily. When you do, you will experience a power and a freedom that you may never have experienced before. It's the power of life in the Spirit. Use it! It's the freedom that Christ died to give you.

7.   It is very important that you begin incorporating the instructions from Romans 6 and 8 into your daily conversations with God. And since there's no better time than the present, begin now. Use the truths you recorded on the Question 3 chart to write out a prayer of commitment that incorporates these truths. To help you get started, I've begun this prayer for you. May this be the first of many, many more prayers just like it.

Insight

Dear Lord,

Today I recognize and consider myself as dead to sin. Because of what Jesus has done for me, I am ready, willing and able to live for Your glory. I will not allow sin to control me, and

_____

_____

_____

_____

_____

_____

_____

The Temple

Day Four

1. This week you've been studying how to experience victory over your sinful nature through the power of the Holy Spirit. In the ongoing war between the flesh and the spirit, God has given us strength to face each battle and win. Give Him glory as you prayerfully praise Him for His strength, His power, and His might.

> *Who is the King of glory?*
> *The Lord strong and mighty,*
> *The Lord mighty in battle.*
> Psalm 24:8 *NASB*

Some of the strongest women I know are physically frail, in wheelchairs, or taking chemo. Yet the supernatural power and strength of the Holy Spirit overwhelms and overshadows their physical weakness.

Whether you're 18 or 88, whether your health is good or not-so-good, whether you're a single woman, a married woman, a mom, or a single mom, God's Word says you can become stronger and stronger every day of your life through the indwelling power of the Holy Spirit.

You've read the command again and again throughout this study: "glorify God in your body" (1 Corinthians 6:20 *NASB*). Glorify God. It's only possible by the power of His Spirit. Today I want you to rejoice as you study the Powerful Presence within you, and remember: there's *no* age limitation, there's *no* physical you must pass, and there's *no* circumstance in life that can disqualify you from experiencing the supernatural, never-ending, all-sufficient power of the Holy Spirit!

2. Begin your study of the Holy Spirit by turning back to your Day Two homework and reading again Romans 8:1–16. But this time, please circle the words "Spirit" or "Holy Spirit" each time you see them. Then summarize what you learn about the Holy Spirit on the following list. To help you get started, I've begun this list for you.

The Holy Spirit

1. v. 2 The power of the Spirit has freed me from the power of sin.

_____

_____

_____

_____

_____

_____

_____

_____

_____

_____

_____

_____

_____

_____

3. As you review the list you've made, stop for a few moments and thank the Lord for the glorious power of His Spirit within you.

4. All through the Bible, God promises He will provide His children with power and strength for every circumstance. Please read the following verses, and record the promises contained within them:

   a. Isaiah 40:28–31

   b. 2 Corinthians 4:16

   c. Philippians 4:13

   d. 2 Timothy 1:7–8

   e. 2 Peter 1:3

5. What weaknesses (physical, spiritual, difficult circumstances, etc.) are you currently experiencing in your life?

6. Take time to look up and record word-for-word one final scripture today: Psalm 73:26.

7. How is the Lord encouraging you to respond to your areas of weakness?

_____

_____

_____

_____

_____

_____

_____

_____

_____

— Day Five —

1. One of the most glorious attributes of God is that He stoops to help us. Just think: the sovereign God and Creator of the universe desires to help us. Why? It's very simple: God helps you for the glory of His name. How has He helped you this week? Take a few minutes to prayerfully and specifically thank Him for the way He's helped you. Glorify His name in prayer right now.

Help us, O God of our salvation, for the glory of Thy name;
And deliver us, and forgive our sins, for Thy name's sake.
Psalm 79:9 *NASB*

We've learned so much about the Holy Spirit this week from the writings of the apostle Paul. It's obvious Paul knew a lot about the power of the Spirit. But did Paul just "talk the talk," or did he actually "walk the walk?" Well, I'm sure you know the answer to that question already, but today I think it will really bless you to study Paul's "walk." Paul emphatically proves that *glo-ing* isn't just for us girls!

2. At the beginning of Paul's first letter to the Corinthians, he reminds them about his initial visit and ministry among them. Please read 1 Corinthians 2:1–5, then answer the following questions:

   a. What was Paul's goal when he first visited the Corinthian church (vv. 1–2)?

   b. How did Paul describe himself when he first ministered to the Corinthians (v. 3)?

   c. How did Paul describe his own preaching to them?

   d. What did Paul's shortcomings as a preacher reveal to those who heard him preach?

   e. What does this passage teach you about your shortcomings and weaknesses?

   f. What does this passage teach about the power of the Spirit?

3. One of my favorite passages from Paul's writing is 2 Corinthians 12:1–10. In these verses, Paul describes an experience that changed his life. Please read this passage, then summarize Paul's experience and what he learned from it.

4. Your journal assignment will be a little different this week. But before you begin journaling, I want to ask you a question: what is your greatest area of weakness? After you've determined the answer to that question, take a few moments to reflect back over all you've learned this week about the power of the Holy Spirit and the weakness of your flesh, then journal your answer to this question: How could God use *your* weakness for *His* glory?

My Journal

I believe the Lord has shown me that my greatest weakness is…

_____

_____

_____

_____

_____

_____

_____

_____

_____

_____

I believe God could use this weakness for His glory by…

_____

_____

_____

_____

_____

_____

_____

_____

_____

_____

As I close our lesson this week, I want to share a passage with you from Oswald Chambers' timeless devotional, *My Utmost For His Highest.* To me, it reinforces what we've studied this week.

> We are designed with a great capacity for God; and sin and our individuality are the things that keep us from getting at God. God delivers us from sin: we have to deliver ourselves from individuality, i.e., to present our natural life to God and sacrifice it until it is transformed into a spiritual life by obedience.

> …God will not discipline us, we must discipline ourselves. God will not bring every thought into captivity; we have to do it. Do not say—O Lord, I suffer from wandering thoughts. Don't suffer from wandering thoughts. Stop listening to the tyranny of your individuality and get emancipated.[5]

Amen, Brother Oswald! Don't his words remind you of Paul's?

> *So, dear brothers and sisters, you have no obligation whatsoever to do what your sinful nature urges you to do. For if you keep on following it, you will perish. But if through the power of the Holy Spirit you turn from it and its evil deeds, you will live.*
>
> —Romans 8:12–13 *NLT*

Amen, again! My sister, we've been divinely called and enabled to glorify God in our everyday lives. We *can* make God look good in everything we do, say, and think.

Through the supernatural power of the Holy Spirit within us, let's win the war against our flesh. When we're weak, let's demonstrate that *He* is strong. When we fail and we're tempted to give in to defeat, let's remember we're *free*—we don't have to live under the tyranny of our old, sinful nature any longer.

Freedom. God's glory. Ideals worth fighting for. So are you ready? Come on. Forward march, sister. Let's *glo!*

The Temple: GLO-ING WITH THE FLOW PART II

***Key Principle: We glorify God in our everyday lives
by allowing the power of His Spirit to flow freely through us.***

The Command: _____ —*1 Cor. 6:19–20*

The Corinthians: _____ _____ —*1 Cor. 3:1–3*

Definition of _____ = sarkikos = _____; the person in
whom the _____ is more the ruling principle.[6]

Definition of _____ / _____ _____ = sarx =
sinfulness, proneness to sin, the _____ _____.[7]

The Characteristics: _____ : immature; jealous; strife; immoral; impure; acting like an
_____ _____. *1 Cor. 3:1–3, 2 Cor. 12:20–21*

_____ / _____ _____: *"…immorality, impurity,
sensuality, idolatry, sorcery, enmities, strife, jealousy, outbursts of anger, disputes,
dissensions, factions, envying, drunkenness, carousing, and things like these…"
Gal. 5:19–21 (NASB).*

The Cure for _____ / _____:

1. It's *Not*: By trying your best to _____ the _____ or a _____
    list of dos and don'ts. *Rom. 3:20, 7:15–25*

2. It *Is*: By being _____ by the _____. *Rom. 8:12–13*

The Commands for Spirit-Controlled Living or *How to Glo with the Flow*:

1. _____ yourself from sin through _____ and repentance of sin.
    1 John 1:9

    * _____ confession – Sins against _____ _____.

    * _____ confession – Sins against _____.

    * _____ confession – Sins against _____ _____.

2. _____ yourself dead to sin and able to live for _____ _____.
    Rom. 6:11, Gal. 5:24

    *Do not allow the flesh to _____ _____. *Rom. 6:12*

    *Make no _____ for the _____. *Rom. 13:14, I Pet. 2:11*

    *Put no _____ in the flesh for _____. *Phil. 3:3*

3. _____ _____ to God's control. *Rom. 6:13*

4. _____ to _____ God. *Rom. 6:19*

The Temple: FUTURE GLORY

I've heard about them…but I've never actually met any of them. I'm sure you've heard about them, too. You know them—those people others describe as being "too heavenly minded to be any earthly good." We've all heard about them, but I seriously doubt that we've ever met many of them. Personally, I've never met even one of them!

On the other hand…I've met many people who are "too earthly minded to be any heavenly good." Oh, yeah, I've seen lots of them. And to be honest, I must admit: I've even been one of them at times. You, too? Well, I'm not surprised—and please don't take that as a put-down. It's just the way it is down here on Planet Earth, isn't it?

In these temporary, earthbound bodies, we're very prone to temporary, earthbound thinking—and living. We get stuck in the grind and routine of the present. We get trapped in the thoughts and cares of today. We get caught up and consumed with the temporal. We forget there's more to life than what we can see here on earth. Much more.

This week, we're going to rise above our temporal, earthbound status and set our sights on our eternal, heaven-bound future. And don't worry. There's absolutely no danger of our becoming "too heavenly minded to be any earthly good." In fact, nothing could be further from the Truth:

> *Set your mind on things above, not on earthly things.*
> —Colossians 3:2

The *New Living Translation* says it like this:

> *Let heaven fill your thoughts. Do not think only about things down here on earth.*
> —Colossians 3:2 *NLT*

There you have it. Straight from God's Word. We're actually commanded to be heavenly minded. So, go ahead. Resist the gravitational pull of your earthbound mindset. Change your focus from the temporal reality of the things that are seen to the eternal reality of the unseen—your eternal home and the glory to come. Your future is bright and on that day, you really are gonna *glo, girl!*

THIS WEEK'S
KEY PRINCIPLE:

We glorify God in our everyday lives by keeping an eternal perspective and preparing for the Glory to come.

Day One

1. One sweet day, God's glory will be revealed and revered by everyone in heaven and on earth. Until then, you have the privilege of giving Him glory every day of your life. Exalt Him now in prayer by using today's Psalm as the expression of your heart.

Be exalted, O God, above the highest heavens.
May Your glory shine over all the earth.
Psalm 108:5 *NLT*

Over the past ten weeks, you've seen how God manifested the glory of His presence through Moses, the tabernacle, the temples, His Son, His Spirit, and now through *you*. God's temple on earth today is you because His Spirit lives within you. Your great call in this life, therefore, is to glorify God in your body.

But what will happen to your body, God's temple, when you die? This will be the topic of our study today and, as you're about to see, death is only the beginning of the glory to come.

2. Unless Jesus comes and the rapture occurs in our lifetime (we'll study the rapture tomorrow), the scriptures say, "it is appointed for men to die once and after this comes judgment," Hebrews 9:27 *(NASB)*. How can we prepare now for our eternal future? Jesus has given us the answer to this question. Please read the scriptures listed on the following chart, then record what Jesus taught about preparing for eternity:

How To Prepare For Eternity

Matthew 5:19–20
Matthew 6:1–4
Matthew 6:5–8
Matthew 6:9–15
Matthew 6:16–18

Matthew 6:19–21
Matthew 7:1–5
Matthew 7:21

3. As you observe the chart you just completed:

   a. In what ways are you currently readying yourself and preparing for eternity?

   b. In what ways is the Lord encouraging you to be better prepared for eternity?

4. Please read 2 Corinthians 5:1–9, then answer the following questions:

   a. According to verse 1, what can we know about death and eternity?

   b. According to verse 5, what has God given to us to assure us of our eternal security?

   c. According to verses 6 and 8, what will occur immediately after we die?

   d. According to verse 9, how can we prepare now for eternity?

The Temple

Now we're going to study what you and I can confidently look forward to after death. In his excellent Greek word study tool, *The Complete Word Study Dictionary New Testament*, Spiros Zodhiates says,

> The true glory of man…is the ideal condition in which God created man. This condition was lost in the fall and is recovered through Christ and exists as a real fact in the divine mind. The believer waits for this complete restoration. The glory of God is what He is essentially; the glory of created things including man is what they are meant by God to be, though not yet perfectly attained.[1]

Although God sees us as though we are already "raised…up with Christ and seated…with Him in the heavenly realms in Christ Jesus," (Ephesians 2:6), every day we see the evidence that our physical bodies are deteriorating and our old, sinful nature is still alive and active. After death, however, we'll see *then* what God sees *now*—glorified, sinless, perfect bodies. For the Christian, death will truly be the beginning of life as God originally intended it to be.

5. Please read 1 Corinthians 15:42-44 and record how our body on earth compares with the glorified body that we will receive in heaven.

It was on earth　　　　　　　**_It will be in heaven_**

6. How will our bodies be transformed? Please read Philippians 3:20–21, and record your answer.

7. How did Paul view life and death? Please read Philippians 1:19–24, and record your answer.

8. As a result of all that you've studied today, what kind of attitude should you have regarding life and death?

_____

_____

_____

_____

_____

_____

_____

_____

_____

_____

— ❧ *Day Two* ❧ —

1. Today's Psalm foretells Christ's return to the earth. Hallelujah, He is coming again! Until then, however, submit yourself to His rule and reign in your life today, as you spend some time on your knees in prayer.

And the nations will tremble before the Lord.
The kings of the earth will tremble before His glory.
For the Lord will rebuild Jerusalem.
He will appear in His glory.
Psalm 102:15–16 *NLT*

Not everyone will experience death. The Bible teaches that prior to the seven-year period of God's judgment and wrath upon this earth (the tribulation), Christ will appear to remove those who belong to Him from the earth. This event is called "the rapture."

Today you'll be studying the rapture and what we'll be experiencing in heaven as the tribulation occurs upon the earth. Please know this: the rapture could occur at any moment—an exciting prospect for those who are ready. Girl, more glory than we've ever seen is on its way—and it could arrive even today.

2. Please read what Paul wrote in 1 Thessalonians 4:13–18, and answer the following questions: **NOTE: Those referred to as "asleep" in verses 13–15, are Christians who have died prior to the rapture.**

   a. What group of people is Paul addressing in this passage? Please circle the correct answer:

      Christians   non-Christians   Christians and non-Christians

   b. What two things did Paul state he believed (v. 14)?

   c. How will the rapture occur (vv. 16–17)?

   d. As you read Paul's words in this passage, when do you think he believed the rapture would occur?

   e. What can you learn from Paul's outlook about the rapture?

3. Please read another brief passage written by Paul that will give you more insight regarding the rapture: 1 Corinthians 15:51–54. Record your answers to the following questions:

   NOTE: When Paul uses the word "mystery," he is referring to something that was not previously revealed in the Old Testament.

   a. What will *not* happen to all believers (v. 51)?

   b. What *will* happen to all believers (v. 51)?

   c. Describe how this will happen (vv. 52–53).

d.   What will the rapture accomplish (v. 54)?

4.   Immediately following the rapture of the church, the tribulation will begin on earth. To discover what will be happening in heaven during this time, please read the following passages, and record your insights:

a.   Romans 14:10–12

b.   2 Corinthians 5:10

c.   1 Corinthians 3:8

d.   Colossians 3:23–25

5.   How do these passages apply to you now, and how do they encourage you in your Christian walk today?

6.   Following the Judgment Seat of Christ, a beautiful event will take place. Please read Revelation 19:7–8 to learn more about this event, then record your insights:

7.   Revelation 19:7–9 refers to the "Lamb" and the "bride." Please read Ephesians 5:25–32, observing how it parallels Revelation 19:7–9, then fill in the following blanks:

      The Lamb in Revelation is _____.
      The bride in Revelation is _____.

8. What insights or applications for your own life has the Holy Spirit revealed to you through your study today?

_____

_____

_____

_____

_____

_____

_____

— Day Three —

1. Can you imagine what it will be like when today's Psalm is reality?! Until then, worship Him today in prayer and praise. Give Him glory.

Everything on earth will worship You;
they will sing Your praises,
shouting Your name in glorious songs.
Psalm 66:4 *NLT*

Today you'll be studying Christ's return to the earth—the second coming and the millennial reign of Christ. I believe the scriptures teach the second coming of Christ will immediately follow the seven-year period of tribulation. The second coming will usher in the millennial reign of Christ. For 1000 years, the glory of God's visible, literal presence will dwell upon the earth. It will be a time unlike any era before it.

Over two thousand years ago, Jesus came to the earth as the Lamb of God who was slain for the sins of the world. When He returns, He will come as the Lion of Judah and *He will reign. Glory, glory!*

2. Revelation 19:11–20:10 and Zechariah 14 are two of the major biblical passages that describe the events of the second coming and the millennial reign of Christ. Using the following chart, please read the passages given, then summarize the various events included in these passages.

The Events of the Second Coming	The Events of the Millennial Reign
Revelation 19:11–20:3	Revelation 20:4–10
Zechariah 14:1–8, 12–15	Zechariah 14:9–11, 16–21

3. To discover the role of the believer during the period of the millennium, please read 1 Corinthians 6:2–3, and briefly summarize what you learn.

4. What will life on earth be like during the millennial reign of Christ? One of the best passages that sums up the answer to this question is Isaiah 65:17–25. Please take a few minutes to read this passage, then briefly record what you learn about life during the millennium. **NOTE: Although Isaiah refers to the "new heaven and new earth" in this passage, most scholars believe this passage describes the millennial kingdom and not the eternal kingdom described in Revelation 21–22.**

Life During The Millennium

_____

_____

_____

_____

_____

_____

_____

_____

_____

_____

_____

_____

You've studied several very detailed passages today, but you still may have more questions than answers about the second coming and the millennium. Please know that even the most well-educated, well-trained theologians don't have all of the answers to the questions these passages unveil. However, I do hope you've been able to see the "big picture" of the glory that will one day return to earth at the second coming and the millennial reign of Christ.

5. There are a few final questions I'd like you to consider. Please review Revelation 20:7–10, then answer these questions:

   a.   What will occur at the conclusion of the millennium (vv. 7–8)?

   b.   What does this reveal about mankind?

   c.   What, perhaps, is God's ultimate purpose for the millennium?

6. In light of all that you've studied today, what have you learned about God?

   _____

   _____

   _____

   _____

   _____

   _____

   _____

   _____

   _____

   _____

— ❧ *Day Four* ❧ —

1. Today's Psalm is prophetic. It speaks of the time when every nation on earth will give glory to the one true God. Despite today's headlines, despite the current conditions of our world, rejoice in prayer by thanking Him for the glorious future that is ours because He is who He is—*God.*

> *All the nations You have made will come and worship*
> *before You, O Lord; they will bring glory to Your name.*
> Psalm 86:9

Our study today will focus on our beautiful, eternal home: heaven. It's a land beyond our comprehension. It's a city custom-designed by the greatest architect of all time. It's built by the One who laid the foundation of the world. It's created by the master carpenter whose nail-pierced hands bear the scars of our sins. His budget is unlimited. His materials are priceless. And He bought and paid for it all with His blood. It's heaven. It's home. And it's glory because, best of all…*He'll* be there!

2. Begin your study today by reading Jesus' words from John 14:1–6 as though you were standing among His disciples and were hearing these words for the very first time.

3. Using the information from verses you just read, please complete the following sentences:

a. Heaven is a place Jesus says….

b. To get to heaven, Jesus says you must…

c. Jesus has promised He…

4. Spend some time in the scriptures studying your future home. Please read Revelation 21:1–4, Revelation 21:10–27, and Revelation 22:1–5. As you read, summarize the highlights of what you learn about your heavenly home.

Future Glory: My Heavenly Home

_____

_____

_____

_____

_____

_____

_____

_____

_____

_____

_____

_____

_____

_____

_____

_____

_____

_____

_____

_____

_____

_____

_____

_____

_____

_____

_____

_____

_____

_____

_____

_____

_____

5. Please review Revelation 21:22–23 and note what you learn about the temple and the glory of God.

6. As you've studied your eternal home today, what truths have you learned about it that have blessed and encouraged you the most?

7. I trust that your heart is full of joy and gratitude to God for the glorious future you will one day share with Him. Express your heart to Him now by writing out a simple, sincere prayer of thanks.

_____

_____

_____

_____

_____

_____

_____

_____

Day Five

1. This week you've studied our glorious future. You've read about heaven, and you've probably even tried to imagine what it will look like. Before you begin your final day of this study, glorify God in prayer for the glorious place He's preparing for you.

> *We had heard of the city's glory, but now we have seen it ourselves—the city of the Lord Almighty. It is the city of our God; He will make it safe forever.*
> Psalm 48:8 *NLT*

You did it! By God's grace and help, you made it to the final day of this study! ***I am so proud of you, and I am so thankful to the Lord for you!*** I would give almost anything to sit down with you one-on-one to hear all about what the Lord has done in your life these past ten weeks as you have diligently studied His Word. One glorious day, we will!

Thank you for your faithfulness from Week One to Week Ten. Thank you for laboring to work through each lesson. Thank you for giving hour upon hour of your time to dig in to the riches of His Word.

How I pray that you've gained a greater understanding of who you are—God's temple—and of the vision and call God has for you—to glorify Him in your everyday life. But, most of all, I pray that you are already beginning to see the results of the transformational power of His Spirit in your life and that others, as well, are witnessing the light of God's glory *glo-ing* through you.

Today's homework will be a day of encouragement, reflection, and thanksgiving. As you complete this final assignment, please feel free—as many times as you are led—to put down this workbook and your pen so that you can lift your hands to give Him glory and praise.

2. There are several promises that I think will bless you on this final day of our study together. Please read the following verses, and record the promises they contain:

a. Matthew 13:43

b. 2 Thessalonians 2:14

c. Jude 24–25 (Note what God is able to do for you.)

d. Revelation 3:12

3. As you read the following scriptures, I want you to see the view God has had from His temple these past ten weeks:

> *The Lord is in His holy temple; the Lord is on His heavenly throne. He observes the sons of men; His eyes examine them.*
>
> —Psalm 11:4

God has carefully been watching you.

> *The Lord looks down from heaven on the sons of men, to see if there are any who understand, any who seek God.*
>
> —Psalm 14:2

As He has watched you, He has seen you seeking Him. He has seen you growing in your understanding of His glory. He has watched you as you have learned to glorify Him. This is the response He longs to receive from you:

With all of my heart I will praise You, O Lord my God. I will give glory to Your name forever.

—Psalm 86:12 *NLT*

Won't you take a few moments to praise Him right now and to commit to be a temple that gives Him glory forever?

4. As your final assignment of this study, please spend the rest of your time today reflecting upon the past ten weeks and journaling the ways you've seen God at work in your life. Perhaps it might help you to flip slowly through the pages of this workbook to reflect upon and review previous lessons you've studied and insights you've written on your journal pages. Or maybe it would help you to review the chart you completed in Week One (Day One, Question 5) where you defined the various areas of your life, and use today's journal to update how God has been "re-defining" you through your study of *The Temple.*

Or if you'd like to just begin freely journaling your thoughts right now, go right ahead. Above all, let this final journal entry be a record that glorifies God.

My Journal

OVER THE LAST TEN WEEKS THE LORD…

_____

_____

_____

_____

_____

_____

_____

_____

_____

_____

_____

_____

_____

_____

_____

_____

_____

_____

AS A RESULT, I…

_____
_____
_____
_____
_____
_____
_____
_____
_____
_____
_____
_____
_____
_____
_____
_____
_____
_____

Dear sister,

I write this final page with tears in my eyes. They're tears of love and gratitude for you. What a privilege it has been to walk with you through the awesome, inspiring, life-changing pages of God's Word these past ten weeks. My tears are also tears of love and gratitude for God who has patiently walked and guided us throughout every step of our study together.

Our key passage for this study has become very familiar to both of us:

> *Or do you not know that your body is a temple of the Holy Spirit who is in you, whom you have from God, and that you are not your own? For you have been bought with a price: therefore glorify God in your body.*
>
> —1 Corinthians 6:19–20 *NASB*

From the very beginning when we started this study, God used it to reawaken me to the miraculous reality of His presence *in me*—His temple. As a result, I have a greater desire than before to move out of His way so He can be glorified in my everyday life. I trust you do, too.

As I was reading my Bible the other day, I came across a passage in the Psalms. Almost immediately, I knew this was the passage I would share with you as we come to the conclusion of our study together. Although we may part company for the present—we'll no longer be studying God's Word together each day—we'll both continue our journey with God. As we say goodbye and as you read this passage, please try to picture it in your mind (you know how much I like to do that):

> *I…belong to You; You are holding my right hand. You will keep on guiding me with Your counsel, leading me to a **glorious destiny.***
>
> —Psalm 73:23 *NLT*

My sister, take His hand in yours…and I will, too. Because of all we've learned from His Word, we know He will safely guide us by His indwelling presence. But we also know this: He will ultimately lead us to the *very* same place—to our "glorious destiny" with Him. Hallelujah!

Until we meet again, let's keep *glo-ing, girl!*

Your sister,

Laurie

The Temple: FUTURE GLORY

Key Principle: *We glorify God in our everyday lives by keeping an eternal perspective and preparing for the Glory to come.*

I. Past, Present, and Future Glory:

A. Past: *The Glory of...*

- The _____

- _____ / _____ Temple

- _____ Temple

- Jesus' _____ _____

B. Present: *The Glory of...*

- The _____ _____

- The _____ / NT Church

C. Future: *The Glory of...*

- _____ _____ _____ and millennial reign.
  Zech. 12:10, 13:6, 14:4–5, 9

- New _____, new _____, new _____.
  Rev. 21:1–2

- God _____ / _____ among men.
  Rev. 21:3

- God and the Lamb as its _____. *Rev. 21:22*

- God and the Lamb as its _____. *Rev. 21:23*

- _____ bringing their _____ into it.
  Rev. 21:24–26

II. Prophecies & Promises of Future Glory:

A. Prophecies and promises of _____.
   Matthew 24:29–30, 25:31, Luke 24:25–27, 44

B. Prophecies and promises of the _____ _____ _____ _____.
   Isaiah 60:1–3, 63:1–4, Psalm 96–98, Malachi 3:1

C. Prophecies and promises of the _____ _____.
   Revelation 22:7,12,20, 1 John 2:28, Romans 8:18–23, 30

What Will Eternity Be Like?
by J. Dwight Pentecost[3]

A. A life of _____ with Him. *John 14:3*

B. A life of _____. *Rev. 14:13*

C. A life of _____ _____. *1 Cor. 13:12*

D. A life of _____. *Rev. 21:27*

E. A life of _____. *Rev. 21:4*

F. A life of _____. *Rev. 22:3*

G. A life of _____. *Rev. 21:6*

H. A life of _____. *2 Cor. 4:17*

I. A life of _____. *Rev. 19:1*

III. Preparing for Future Glory:

A. Be _____ _____. *Col. 3:2*

B. Be a _____ to the _____. *Acts 1:6-8, 1 Cor. 14:24-25*

C. Be dressed, ready, _____ and _____ in Him.
   Luke 12:35-40, Jere. 9:24

Or do you not know that your body is a temple of the Holy Spirit who is in you, whom you have from God, and that you are not your own? For you have been bought with a price: therefore glorify God in your body.

—1 Corinthians 6:19–20 NASB

The Temple: A Change of Heart

If you're wondering whether or not your heart has ever been changed, I sure want to help you settle any doubts you may have regarding your relationship with God. I want you to know that you have received the gift of salvation through Jesus Christ, and I want you to experience the peace and the power of His Spirit in your life today and from this day forward. If what I've just described is your desire, then I hope you'll continue reading so you can experience a real change of heart today.

One of the evidences of true Christianity is a changed heart. God prophesied through the prophet Ezekiel that He would give His people a new heart and a new spirit:

> *I will give you a **new heart** and put a **new spirit** in you; I will remove from you your heart of stone and give you a **heart of flesh**. And I will put My **Spirit** in you and move you to follow My decrees and be careful to keep My laws.*
> —Ezekiel 36:26–27

This prophecy was fulfilled by Jesus Christ through His death on the cross (Matthew 26:26–29). You see, if you want to receive a new heart and a new spirit, you can only receive them through salvation in *Christ alone*.

Salvation isn't the result of being a good person. Salvation isn't even about being a religious person. The Bible says, "For it is **by grace** you have been saved, **through faith**—and this not from yourselves, it is the **gift** of God not by **works**, so that no one can boast" (Ephesians 2:8–9). Salvation is God's gracious gift to you through Christ's work on the cross. The gift of salvation is available to you if you will receive it by faith.

Precious one—
- If you've never experienced a real and lasting change in your heart, life, and spirit;
- If you believe the Lord is convicting you of your need for salvation right now; and
- If you are ready to accept His grace and salvation to you by faith in Him;

then please allow me to lead you to Christ so you can receive the gift of salvation and a true and lasting change of heart:

1. Please read the following scripture, then **confess** to God that you are a sinner and you need a changed heart and a new spirit.

   > *For all have sinned and fall short of the glory of God.*
   > —Romans 3:23

2. Please read the following scriptures, then tell God you **believe** in Him, you desire to give Him your life, and you want to **receive** the gift of salvation through His Son, Jesus Christ.

   > *For the wages of sin is death, but the gift of God is eternal life in Christ Jesus our Lord.*
   > —Romans 6:23

   > *That if you confess with your mouth, 'Jesus is Lord,' and believe in your heart that God raised Him from the dead, you will be saved. For it is with your heart that you believe and are justified, and it is with your mouth that you confess and are saved.*
   > —Romans 10:9–10

3. Finally, take a few minutes to prayerfully thank God for the gift of salvation and for the change He has wrought within your heart and spirit.

My sister, I am so happy for you! You may not realize it yet, but your heart has been changed and His Spirit has come to reside within you. Trust me, you will see the evidence of these changes in your life very soon. God has forgiven you of all of your sins—past, present, and future sins—and He resides now within your heart through His Spirit. Through the indwelling work of His Spirit, He is beginning—right now—a new work in your heart and life.

Because you have become a Christian, I want to encourage you to take your first steps of faith in obedience to Christ:

1. Tell someone about it. You've just read in Romans 10:9–10 that you need to confess Christ as your Lord and Savior. You've done this privately in prayer. Now you need to confess your new relationship with Him publicly. If you're doing this study with a small group, tell your small group leader or someone else in your group. Trust me, you're going to make their day and they're going to rejoice with you.

2. Seek to follow Christ in baptism. Baptism is simply another way to publicly profess your faith in Christ. It symbolizes your "death" to self, and your new life in Christ. Jesus Himself was baptized in obedience to God, and you'll want to follow His example. God will bless your obedience.

3. Become a member of a Christ-centered, Bible-believing church. Ask God to lead you to a loving, healthy church where you'll be spiritually fed, where you can enjoy friendship and fellowship with other Christians and serve Him effectively.

Finally, let me give you one more scripture that describes who you now are, my sister:

Or do you not know that your body is a temple of the Holy Spirit who is in you, whom you have from God, and that you are not your own? For you have been bought with a price: therefore glorify God in your body.

—1 Corinthians 6:19–20 *NASB*

You've become God's temple, and you know what that means. *You glo, girl!*

WEEK ONE—GLORY!

[1]Herbert Lockyer, Sr., ed., *Nelson's Illustrated Bible Dictionary* (Nashville: Thomas Nelson Publishers, 1986), 424.
[2]Ibid.
[3]Ibid.
[4]Ibid

WEEK TWO—SHINE!

[1]John F. Walvoord and Roy B. Zuck, *The Bible Knowledge Commentary*, (Wheaton, IL: Victor Books, 1984), 624.
[2]Spiros Zodhiates, *The Complete Word Study Dictionary New Testament*, (Chattanooga, TN: AMG Publishers, Revised edition 1993), 70.
[3]James Strong, *Strong's Exhaustive Concordance* (Iowa Falls, Iowa: Riverside Book and Bible House), 1984.

WEEK THREE—DETAILS, DETAILS, DETAILS!

[1]Dooley, Tara. "Science of the Soul." Houston Chronicle, 26 June 2004, sec. E, 1 & 4.
[2]Ibid.

WEEK FOUR—SYMBOLS THAT STILL SPEAK

[1]Herbert Lockyer, Sr., ed., *Nelson's Illustrated Bible Dictionary* (Nashville: Thomas Nelson Publishers, 1986), 1077.

WEEK SIX—GREATER GLORY

[1]Spiros Zodhiates, Warren Baker, *The Complete Word Study Dictionary New Testament* (Chattanooga, TN: AMG Publishers, revised edition, 1993), 1295.
[2]Herbert Lockyer, Sr., ed., *Nelson's Illustrated Bible Dictionary* (Nashville: Thomas Nelson Publishers, 1986), 424.
[3]Zodhiates, Baker, *The Complete Word Study Dictionary New Testament*, 478.
[4]Ibid

WEEK EIGHT—GOD'S TEMPLE TODAY—YOU!

[1]Charles Stanley, *The Wonderful Spirit Filled Life* (Nashville, TN: Thomas Nelson Publishers, 1992), 64.

WEEK NINE—GLORIFYING GOD IN THE SPIRIT

[1]John F. Walvoord and Roy B. Zuck, *The Bible Knowledge Commentary*, (Wheaton, IL: Victor Books, 1984), 468.
[2]Spiros Zodhiates, *The Complete Word Study Dictionary New Testament*, (Chattanooga, TN: AMG Publishers, Revised edition 1993), 1280.
[3]John F. Walvoord and Roy B. Zuck, *The Bible Knowledge Commentary*, 463.
[4]Ibid.
[5]Oswald Chambers, *My Utmost For His Highest* (New York: Dodd, Mead & Company), 323.
[6]Spiros Zodhiates, *The Complete Word Study New Testament*, (Chattanooga, TN: AMG Publishers, 1991), 954.
[7]Spiros Zodhiates, *The Complete Word Study Dictionary New Testament*, (Chattanooga, TN: AMG Publishers, Revised edition 1993), 1280.

WEEK TEN—FUTURE GLORY

[1]Spiros Zodhiates, *The Complete Word Study Dictionary New Testament*, (Chattanooga, TN: AMG Publishers, Revised Edition 1993), 478.
[2]J. Dwight Pentecost, *Things To Come: A Study In Biblical Eschatology*, (Grand Rapids, MI: Academie Books, Zondervan Publishing House 1964), 525.
[3]J. Dwight Pentecost, *Things To Come: A Study In Biblical Eschatology*, (Grand Rapids, MI: Academie Books, Zondervan Publishing House 1964), 581-582.

Shop**Priority**

Visit Priority's online store to find out more about Bible studies, DVDs, and CDs by Laurie Cole. Each product will encourage you to give God glory and priority.

Shop online now!
Monday - Friday, 9am - 4pm CST

www.priorityministries.org/shop

AUDIO CD SETS

BEAUTY BY THE BOOK &
BEAUTY BY THE BOOK FOR TEENS
Bible Studies

THERE IS A SEASON
Bible Study

Discover how to become the consistent, contented woman you've always wanted to be in every season of life.

New!
FREE
Video Downloads
for both *Beauty by The Book* studies!

Resources available for these studies:

Workbooks, Small Group CD-ROM Leader Guides,
Video Lectures and Audio Lectures.

Whether you're 17 or 70, learn the secrets of becoming a biblically beautiful woman.

You**GLO**Girl

Priority Ministries' **monthly e-newsletter**, is our opportunity to *glo*—to give God glory—as Laurie Cole and the Priority staff share the latest scoop about Priority Ministries. Visit us online to *subscribe* or read the latest issue.

www.priorityministries.org/glogirl

ConnectWithPriority

Priority Partners believe in the mission of Priority Ministries and support it with their generous financial gifts. Would you prayerfully consider becoming a Partner and helping us reach and teach women to love God most and seek Him first?

Become a monthly or one-time donor. Either way, your financial gifts provide vital support for this ministry! For more information about becoming a Priority Partner, visit our web site:

www.priorityministries.org/support

PrioritySorority

Priority Sorority is an online bulletin board where you can post your praise to God for the way He is working in your life, or read what others are saying about a Priority Bible Study. So, c'mon...join today! Become a Priority Sorority Sister!

How to join:

Visit our web site, www.priorityministries.org, click the *Connect with Priority* link, and click on *Priority Sorority Bulletin Board* to:

- Share your testimony.
- Read other testimonies.
- Be encouraged!

www.priorityministries.org/connect/sorority/sharebboard.php

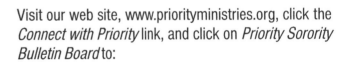

Encouraging Women to Give God Glory & Priority